Contents

Introduction

This course is designed to cover all the topics now included in the Common Core papers of the A-level examination in Mechanics (Modules M1 and M2). Each topic in the course is treated separately, allowing the student to revise an individual topic more easily.

Every section commences with notes relevant to the particular topic, followed by several worked examples. The student should study these carefully and note the principles used and the appropriate methods adopted.

At the end of each section there is a selection of exercises designed to follow the worked examples closely. These should be attempted by the student in conjunction with study of the worked examples. Answers for all questions and hints to solutions are given in the section at the end of the book.

The International System of Units (SI units) will be used throughout the book, and the acceleration due to gravity at the Earth's surface will be taken to be $9.8\,\mathrm{m\,s}^{-2}$ unless otherwise stated.

Chapter 1

Constant acceleration

This chapter deals with motion in a straight line with constant acceleration.

The initial speed is denoted by the letter u.
The final speed is denoted by the letter v.
The acceleration is denoted by the letter a.
The distance covered is denoted by the letter s.
The time taken is denoted by the letter t.

$$v = u + at.$$
$$s = ut + \tfrac{1}{2}at^2.$$
$$s = vt - \tfrac{1}{2}at^2.$$
$$s = \tfrac{1}{2}(u + v)t.$$
$$v^2 = u^2 + 2as.$$

Examples

EXAMPLE

1

A train travelling at $120\,\mathrm{m\,s^{-1}}$ passes a point X. At this instant the brakes are applied, producing a constant retardation during which the train covers 1 km in 10 s, passing a point Y. It continues with this retardation until it is brought to rest into a station Z.

Find: (a) its speed as it passes Y; (b) the magnitude of the constant retardation; (c) the distance from X to Z.

SOLUTION

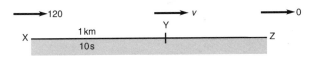

Motion from X to Y

$$u = 120$$
$$t = 10$$
$$s = 1000.$$

Using $s = ut + \tfrac{1}{2}at^2$

$$1000 = (120 \times 10) + (\tfrac{1}{2}a \times 100)$$
$$50a = -200$$
$$\underline{a = -4}.$$

Motion from X to Z

$$u = 120$$
$$v = 0$$
$$a = -4.$$

Using $v^2 = u^2 + 2as$

$$0 = 120^2 - 8s$$
$$\underline{s = 1800}.$$

Using $v = u + at$

$$v = 120 + (-4)10$$

$$\underline{v = 80}.$$

Hence: **(a)** the speed at Y = $\underline{80\,\text{m}\,\text{s}^{-1}}$;

   (b) the retardation = $\underline{4\,\text{m}\,\text{s}^{-2}}$;

   (c) the distance XZ = $\underline{1.8\,\text{km}}$.

EXAMPLE

2

A particle moves in a straight line ABC with constant acceleration. It moves from A to B, a distance of 40 m, in 2 s and then from B to C, a distance of 560 m, in 8 s.

Find: (a) the speeds of the particle as it passes A, B and C; (b) the magnitude of the acceleration.

SOLUTION

Motion from A to B

$$s = 40$$

$$t = 2.$$

Using $s = ut + \frac{1}{2}at^2$

$$40 = 2u + 2a$$

$$\underline{20 = u + a}.$$

Motion from A to C

$$s = 600$$

$$t = 10.$$

Using $s = ut + \frac{1}{2}at^2$

$$600 = 10u + 50a$$

$$\underline{60 = u + 5a}.$$

Solving these two equations we obtain $\underline{u = 10}$ and $\underline{a = 10}$.

Using $v = u + at$

$$v = 10 + 20$$

$$\underline{v = 30}.$$

Using $v = u + at$

$$w = 10 + 100$$

$$\underline{w = 110}.$$

Hence: **(a)** the speeds at A, B and C are $\underline{10\,\text{m}\,\text{s}^{-1}}$, $\underline{30\,\text{m}\,\text{s}^{-1}}$ and $\underline{110\,\text{m}\,\text{s}^{-1}}$;

   (b) the constant acceleration = $\underline{10\,\text{m}\,\text{s}^{-2}}$.

EXAMPLE

3

A particle moves in a straight line ABC, starting from rest at A and moving with constant acceleration $4k$ until it reaches B. It then continues from B to C with constant acceleration k.

If the time taken from B to C is twice the time taken from A to B, find: (a) the ratio of the speeds at C and B; (b) the ratio of the distance BC to AB.

SOLUTION

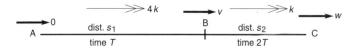

Motion from A to B	Motion from B to C
$s = s_1$	$s = s_2$
$a = 4k$	$a = k$
$t = T$	$t = 2T.$
$u = 0.$	Using $v = u + at$
Using $v = u + at$	$w = v + k \cdot 2T$
$\underline{v = 4kT.}$	$\underline{w = 6kT.}$
Using $s = \frac{1}{2}(u+v)t$	Using $s = \frac{1}{2}(u+v)t$
$s_1 = \frac{1}{2}(4kT)T$	$s_2 = \frac{1}{2}(10kT)2T$
$\underline{s_1 = 2kT^2.}$	$\underline{s_2 = 10kT^2.}$

Hence: **(a)** the ratio of the speeds at C and B $= w:v = \underline{3:2}$;

(b) the ratio of the distance BC to AB $= 10kT^2 : 2kT^2 = \underline{5:1}.$

EXAMPLE

4

A small stone X is allowed to fall from rest from a point at the top of a cliff. Two seconds later a similar small stone Y is projected vertically downwards from the same point with a speed of $24\,\text{m}\,\text{s}^{-1}$. Both X and Y reach the foot of the cliff at the same time.

By modelling the stones as particles and taking $g = 10\,\text{m}\,\text{s}^{-2}$, find: (a) the time of descent of X; (b) the height of the cliff; (c) the speeds with which X and Y reach the foot of the cliff.

SOLUTION   Let the time of descent of Y be T seconds. Hence the time of descent of X is $(T + 2)$ seconds.

Let the height of the cliff be $h\,\text{m}$.

Motion of X	Motion of Y	
$s = h$	$s = h$	
$t = (T + 2)$	$t = T$	
$a = g$	$a = g$	
$u = 0.$	$u = 24.$	
Using $s = ut + \frac{1}{2}at^2$	Using $s = ut + \frac{1}{2}at^2$	
$h = 0 + 5(T+2)^2.$	$h = 24T + 5T^2.$	

Hence
$$5(T + 2)^2 = 24T + 5T^2$$
$$5T^2 + 20T + 20 = 24T + 5T^2$$
$$4T = 20$$
$$\underline{T = 5} \Rightarrow \underline{h = 245\,\text{m}.}$$

Using $v = u + at$	Using $v = u + at$
$v = 0 + 10(7)$	$w = 24 + 10(5)$
$\underline{v = 70.}$	$\underline{w = 74.}$

Hence: **(a)** the time of descent for X is 7 s;

(b) the height of the cliff $= 245$ m;

(c) the speeds of X and Y at the foot are $70\,\mathrm{m\,s^{-1}}$ and $74\,\mathrm{m\,s^{-1}}$.

EXAMPLE 5

A car is travelling along a level road at a constant speed of $126\,\mathrm{km\,h^{-1}}$. The driver sees traffic lights ahead of him turn to red. It takes him 3 s to react to the situation and then he applies his brakes so as to produce a constant retardation.

If he brings the car to rest at the lights 10 s after he saw the lights turn to red, find: (a) the distance from the lights when he saw them change to red; (b) the magnitude of the retardation produced by the brakes.

SOLUTION

The first 3 s of the motion is at constant speed.

The speed of $126\,\mathrm{km\,h^{-1}}$ must be converted into $\mathrm{m\,s^{-1}}$.

$3.6\,\mathrm{km\,h^{-1}}$ is equal to $1\,\mathrm{m\,s^{-1}}$.

Hence the speed of the car is $126 \div 3.6 = 35\,\mathrm{m\,s^{-1}}$.

The distance travelled in the first 3 s $= 35 \times 3 = \underline{105\,\mathrm{m}}$.

Motion during retardation

$u = 35$

$v = 0$

$t = 7.$

Using $s = \frac{1}{2}(u+v)t$

$\qquad s = \frac{1}{2}(35+0)7$

$\qquad \underline{s = 122\frac{1}{2}.}$

Using $v = u + at$

$\qquad 0 = 35 + 7a$

$\qquad \underline{a = -5.}$

Hence: **(a)** the distance to the lights $= 227\frac{1}{2}$ m;

(b) the magnitude of the retardation $= 5\,\mathrm{m\,s^{-2}}$.

EXAMPLE 6

A car is travelling at a steady speed of $20\,\mathrm{m\,s^{-1}}$ when it passes a police patrol car at a point A. The police immediately give chase, accelerating uniformly from rest to a maximum speed of $30\,\mathrm{m\,s^{-1}}$ in 40 s. They then continue at this speed of $30\,\mathrm{m\,s^{-1}}$ for a further T seconds, finally decelerating to rest, arriving at a point B. The car had continued at its steady speed of $20\,\mathrm{m\,s^{-1}}$ for 1 min but then, realising it is being chased, it decelerates uniformly, also coming to rest at B at the same instant as the police.

Sketch on the same axes the velocity–time graphs for the two cars.

If the distance AB is 1.5 km, find: (a) the total time of the chase; (b) the value of T.

SOLUTION

Let the time during which the car decelerates be t seconds.

The *total* area under each graph represents the distance covered.

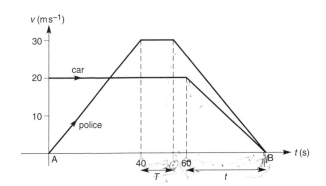

Motion of car

Total area $= (60 \times 20) + \frac{1}{2}(20t)$

$1500 = 1200 + 10t$

$\underline{t = 30}.$

Motion of police

Total area $= \frac{1}{2}(40 \times 30) + 30T + \frac{1}{2}(50 - T) \times 30$

$1500 = 600 + 30T + 750 - 15T$

$150 = 15T$

$\underline{T = 10}.$

Hence: **(a)** the total time of the chase is $\underline{90\,s}$;

(b) the value of $\underline{T = 10}$.

Exercises

1 A car is moving along a straight, level road with constant acceleration. It passes two points A and B at speeds of $4\,\mathrm{m\,s^{-1}}$ and $12\,\mathrm{m\,s^{-1}}$ respectively in 20 s.

Find: (a) the distance AB; (b) the magnitude of the acceleration.

2 A particle travelling in a straight line with constant acceleration passes a point A at a speed u. After travelling 120 m in 6 s, it passes a point B. Four seconds later, after covering a further distance of 60 m, it passes through a point C.

Find: (a) the value of u; (b) the retardation of the particle; (c) the speeds of the particle at B and C.

3 A car starts from rest at a point X on a straight, level road and moves with constant acceleration until it reaches its maximum speed of $144\,\mathrm{km\,h^{-1}}$ in 10 s. It then continues for 15 s at this maximum speed until it reaches a point Y. At the instant the car starts, it is overtaken by a motor cyclist travelling at a constant speed of $108\,\mathrm{km\,h^{-1}}$.

By modelling the car and the cyclist as particles, find: (a) the acceleration of the car; (b) the distance XY.

Does the car overtake the cyclist between X and Y?

4 A particle, which is moving in a straight line with constant acceleration, passes through points O, A and B at times $t = 0$, $t = 1$ and $t = 2$ s respectively.

If OA $= 10$ m and AB $= 20$ m, find: (a) the speed of the particle at O; (b) the magnitude of the acceleration.

5 A particle starts from rest at a point A and moves in a straight line, passing through points A, B, C and D in that order. $AB = 100\,m$, $BC = 60\,m$ and $CD = 20\,m$. From A to B it accelerates at $2\,m\,s^{-2}$. From B to C it travels at a constant speed, and then from C to D it retards uniformly to rest.

Find: (a) the total time from A to D; (b) the magnitude of the retardation from C to D.

6 A small stone A is projected vertically upwards with a speed of $147\,m\,s^{-1}$. At the same instant, another small stone B is allowed to fall from rest from a point vertically above the point of projection of A. The stones collide when they have each travelled the same distance.

Find: (a) the time that elapses before collision; (b) the initial distance between the stones.

7 A particle travelling with constant acceleration in a straight line passes through points A, B and C in that order. It takes 2 s to travel from A to B, a distance of 90 m. It takes 4 s to travel from B to C, a distance of 240 m.

Find: (a) the magnitude of the acceleration of the particle; (b) its speed as it passes through C.

8 Two cars X and Y are travelling in the same direction along a main road. They pass a sign at the same instant indicating a 'halt' will come very soon at an intersection 1.5 km away. They subsequently arrive at the halt at the same time. Car X passes the sign at $20\,m\,s^{-1}$ and continues at this speed for 1 min, finally decelerating uniformly to rest at the halt. Car Y passes the sign at $30\,m\,s^{-1}$ and continues at this speed for T s and finally decelerates uniformly to rest at the halt.

Sketch *on the same axes* the speed–time graphs for each car.

Find: (a) the total time taken by the cars to reach the halt; (b) the value of T.

Chapter 2

Friction

Friction is a force which acts only when required.

The friction force can take any value from zero to a maximum value that is proportional to the normal contact force.

Max $F = \mu R$.

R is the normal contact force and μ is a constant called the 'coefficient of friction', its value varying for different surfaces.

A perfectly smooth surface will have $\mu = 0$, thus causing no friction.

When the maximum friction force has been reached, equilibrium is said to be 'limiting'.

In equilibrium:	$F \leq \mu R$.
In limiting equilibrium:	$F = \mu R$.
When in motion:	$F = \mu R$.

Examples

EXAMPLE

1

A mass of 2 kg rests on a rough plane inclined at an angle α to the horizontal.

If the coefficient of friction is $\frac{1}{2}$, find the largest value of α, to the nearest degree, for which equilibrium can be maintained.

SOLUTION

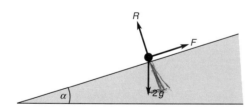

Resolve perp. to plane	Resolve parallel to plane	For equilibrium
$R = 2g \cos \alpha$.	$F = 2g \sin \alpha$.	$F \leq \mu R$.

Hence $2g \sin \alpha \leq \frac{1}{2}(2g \cos \alpha)$

$\qquad \tan \alpha \leq \frac{1}{2}$

$\qquad \underline{\underline{\alpha \leq 26°}}$.

EXAMPLE

2

A particle of mass 0.5 kg rests on a rough plane inclined at an angle α to the horizontal, where $\tan \alpha = 0.75$.

If the coefficient of friction is $\frac{1}{2}$, find: (a) the *smallest* force acting up the plane to maintain equilibrium; (b) the *largest* force acting up the plane which does not destroy equilibrium.

SOLUTION

(a) *Resolve perp. to plane*
$R = 0.5g \cos \alpha.$

Resolve parallel to plane
$P_1 + F = 0.5g \sin \alpha.$

Limiting friction
$F = \mu R.$

Hence $P_1 + \frac{1}{4}g(0.8) = \frac{1}{2}g(0.6)$

$$P_1 = 0.98 \text{ N.}$$

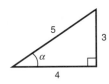

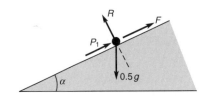

(b) *Resolve perp. to plane*
$R = 0.5g \cos \alpha.$

Resolve parallel to plane
$P_2 - F = 0.5g \sin \alpha.$

Limiting friction
$F = \mu R.$

Hence $P_2 - \frac{1}{4}g(0.8) = \frac{1}{2}g(0.6)$

$$P_2 = 4.9 \text{ N.}$$

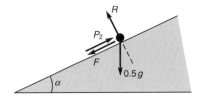

EXAMPLE

3

A particle of mass 0.5 kg rests on a rough plane inclined at an angle α to the horizontal, where $\tan \alpha = 0.75$.

If the coefficient of friction is $\frac{1}{8}$, find the smallest *horizontal* force that can be applied so as to maintain equilibrium.

SOLUTION

Resolve perp. to plane
$R = P \sin \alpha + 0.5g \cos \alpha.$

Resolve parallel to plane
$F + P \cos \alpha = 0.5g \sin \alpha.$

Limiting friction
$F = \mu R.$

Hence $\frac{1}{8}(0.6P + 3.92) + 0.8P = 2.94$

$$P = 2.8 \text{ N.}$$

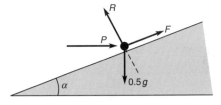

EXAMPLE

4

A particle of mass 0.4 kg rests on a rough plane inclined at an angle α to the horizontal, where $\tan \alpha = \frac{5}{12}$.

If the coefficient of friction is $\frac{1}{8}$, find the greatest *horizontal* force that can be applied without destroying equilibrium.

SOLUTION   *Resolve perp. to plane*   *Resolve parallel to plane*   *Limiting friction*

$R = P \sin \alpha + 0.4g \cos \alpha.$ $P \cos \alpha = F + 0.4g \sin \alpha.$ $F = \mu R.$

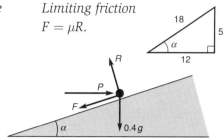

Hence $P \cos \alpha = \mu(P \sin \alpha + 0.4g \cos \alpha) + 0.4g \sin \alpha$

$P(\cos \alpha - \mu \sin \alpha) = 0.4g(\mu \cos \alpha + \sin \alpha)$

$$\underline{\underline{P = 2.24\,\text{N}.}}$$

EXAMPLE 5

A uniform ladder, mass 10 kg and length $2a$, rests with one end A against a smooth vertical wall, while the other end B rests on rough horizontal ground. The ladder is in a vertical plane perpendicular to the wall.

If the coefficient of friction is $\frac{1}{7}$ and the ladder is on the point of slipping, find: (a) the inclination of the ladder to the horizontal (nearest degree); (b) the normal contact force of the ground on the ladder; (c) the reaction of the wall on the ladder.

SOLUTION   *Resolve horizontally*   *Resolve vertically*   *Limiting friction*

$F = S.$ $R = 10g.$ $F = \mu R$
                              $F = \mu(10g).$

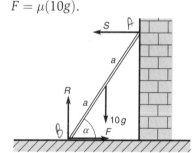

Taking moments about B

$S\,2a \sin \alpha = 10g\,a \cos \alpha$

$S = \frac{1}{2}(10g \cot \alpha)$

$\mu 10g = \frac{1}{2}(10g \cot \alpha)$

$\tan \alpha = \frac{7}{2}$

$$\underline{\underline{\alpha = 74.}}$$

Hence: **(a)** the inclination of the ladder to the horizontal $= \underline{\underline{74°}}$;
        (b) the reaction of the ground $= \underline{\underline{98\,\text{N}}}$;
        (c) the reaction of the wall $= \underline{\underline{14\,\text{N}}}$.

EXAMPLE 6

Two equal rings A and B, each weighing $3W$, can move along a fixed, rough, horizontal curtain rail, the coefficient of friction being $\frac{1}{4}$. The rings are connected by a light, smooth, inextensible string of length 6 m, which hangs below the rail and has a smooth ring C of weight $2W$, which can move freely on it. The ring C rests in equilibrium below the rail.

Find the maximum possible distance between the rings A and B.

SOLUTION

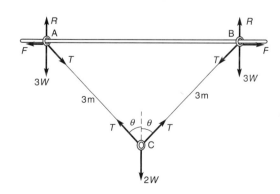

Resolve vertically for C

$2T \cos \theta = 2W$

$T \cos \theta = W.$

Resolve horizontally for A

$F = T \sin \theta$

$F = W \tan \theta.$

Resolve vertically for A

$R = 3W + T \cos \theta$

$R = 4W.$

Limiting friction at A

$F = \mu R$

$F = \frac{1}{4}(4W)$

$F = W.$

Hence $\tan \theta = 1$

$\theta = 45°.$

Hence the maximum distance between A and B $= 3 \cos 45° \times 2$

$$= 3\sqrt{2}.$$

The maximum distance between A and B for equilibrium $= \underline{\underline{3\sqrt{2}\,\text{m}}}.$

Exercises

1   A particle of mass 0.5 kg rests on a rough plane inclined at an angle α to the horizontal.

If the coefficient of friction is $\frac{1}{4}$, find the greatest value of α, to the nearest degree, for which equilibrium can be maintained.

2   A particle of mass 0.8 kg lies on a rough plane, its inclination being $\tan^{-1}(0.75)$ to the horizontal.

If the coefficient of friction is 0.1, find: (a) the least force acting up the plane to maintain equilibrium; (b) the greatest force acting up the plane that can be applied without destroying equilibrium.

3   A particle of mass 0.3 kg rests on a rough plane inclined at an angle α to the horizontal, where $\tan \alpha = \frac{8}{15}$.

If the coefficient of friction is $\frac{1}{6}$, find the smallest horizontal force that can be applied if equilibrium is to be maintained.

4   A uniform ladder XY, mass 12 kg and length 6 m, lies with its end X on rough, horizontal ground and its other end Y against a smooth, vertical wall. The ladder rests in a vertical plane perpendicular to the wall.

If the coefficient of friction between the ground and the ladder is 0.6, find: (a) the smallest angle that the ladder can make with the horizontal; (b) the reaction of the wall when the ladder is about to slip.

5 A uniform ladder of mass 150 kg rests with one end against a smooth wall and its other end on rough, horizontal ground, the coefficient of friction being $\frac{1}{2}$. The ladder rests in a vertical plane perpendicular to the wall.

Show that the ladder will not rest if it is inclined at α to the horizontal, where $\tan\alpha = 0.75$.

What is the mass of the lightest boy who could stand on the ladder at its base so that equilibrium could be maintained at this angle?

6 A rough plane can be inclined at different angles to the horizontal. When inclined at an angle θ to the horizontal, where $\tan\theta = \frac{3}{4}$, a particle of mass m slides down the plane at a constant speed. When inclined at an angle ϕ to the horizontal, where $\tan\phi = \frac{4}{3}$, the particle moves down the plane with an acceleration $a\,\mathrm{m\,s^{-2}}$.

Find the value of the acceleration a in terms of g.

7 A fixed, rough plane is inclined at an angle θ to the horizontal, the coefficient of friction being $\frac{1}{3}$. A particle of mass m is on the point of moving *down* the plane when a force P acts on it up the plane. The particle is on the point of moving *up* the plane when a force $2P$ acts on it up the plane.

Find the value of θ.

8 A particle P of mass $3m$ rests on rough, horizontal ground. One end of a light, inelastic string is attached to P, while another particle Q of mass $2m$ is attached to its other end. The string passes over a smooth pulley fixed at a height of 12 m above the ground and at a horizontal distance of 5 m from P. Q hangs below the pulley with the string taut and the system in limiting equilibrium.

Find the value of μ, the coefficient of friction between the ground and P.

9 A particle P of weight W rests on a rough plane inclined at $45°$ to the horizontal. When a horizontal force T is applied to the particle, it just prevents it slipping *down* the plane. If the same force T is now applied up the plane instead of horizontally, the particle would be on the point of moving *up* the plane.

Find μ, the coefficient of friction between the particle and the plane, answering to three significant figures.

Chapter 3

Newton's laws of motion

This chapter deals with Newton's laws, in particular his second law, commonly called Newton's equation of motion:

$F = ma.$

> **Law 1:** A body remains at rest or in uniform linear motion unless acted upon by an external force.
>
> **Law 2:** The change in momentum of a body is proportional to the impressed force and acts in its direction.
>
> **Law 3:** Action and reaction are equal and opposite.

Examples

EXAMPLE 1

A car of mass 1 tonne starts from rest and moves along a level road. The engine of the car produces a constant tractive force of 1.5 kN and the total resistance to the motion is constant and equal to 1.2 kN.

Find: (a) the acceleration of the car; (b) the distance covered in 1 min; (c) the speed developed after 1 min.

SOLUTION

Equation of motion

$$T - F = 1000\,a$$
$$1500 - 1200 = 1000\,a$$
$$\underline{a = 0.3}.$$

$u = 0$	Using $v = u + at$	Using $s = \frac{1}{2}(u+v)t$
$a = 0.3$	$v = 0 + (0.3 \times 60)$	$s = \frac{1}{2}(0 + 18) \times 60$
$t = 60.$	$\underline{v = 18}.$	$\underline{s = 540}.$

(a) The acceleration of the car $= \underline{0.3\,\mathrm{m\,s^{-2}}}$.

(b) The distance travelled in 1 min $= \underline{540\,\mathrm{m}}$.

(c) The speed after 1 min $= \underline{18\,\mathrm{m\,s^{-1}}}$.

EXAMPLE 2

A man of mass 80 kg stands on a weighing machine which is in a lift.

If the lift ascends with an acceleration of $0.2\,\mathrm{m\,s^{-2}}$ what will the dial on the weighing machine register as the man's weight?

What would the machine register if the lift were descending with the same acceleration? (Take $g = 10\,\mathrm{m\,s^{-2}}$.)

SOLUTION   *Equation of motion for man*

$$R - 80g = 80 \times 0.2$$

$$R = 16 + 800$$

$$\underline{R = 816\,\text{N}}.$$

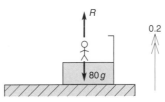

Hence the dial registers $\underline{81.6\,\text{kg}}$ when the lift is ascending.

Equation of motion for man

$$80g - S = 80 \times 0.2$$

$$S = 800 - 16$$

$$\underline{S = 784\,\text{N}}.$$

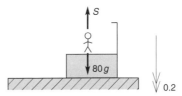

Hence the dial registers $\underline{78.4\,\text{kg}}$ when the lift is descending.

EXAMPLE

3

A van of mass 2 tonnes is ascending a slope, which is inclined at α to the horizontal, where $\sin\alpha = 0.05$. The total resistance to motion is constant and equal to 500 N, while the tractive force of the engine of the van is also constant and equal to 4 kN.

Find the acceleration of the van up the slope.

SOLUTION   *Equation of motion up the slope*

$$P - 2000g\sin\alpha - R = 2000\,a$$

$$4000 - (19\,600 \times 0.05) - 500 = 2000\,a$$

$$2520 = 2000\,a$$

$$\underline{a = 1.26}.$$

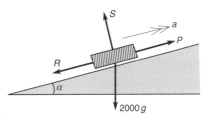

The acceleration of the van up the slope is $\underline{1.26\,\text{m s}^{-2}}$.

EXAMPLE

4

Two small particles X and Y, masses 0.5 kg and 0.3 kg respectively, are attached to the ends of a light, inextensible string, which passes over a smooth, fixed pulley P. Y lies on a fixed, horizontal surface below the pulley and the particle X is held at a height of 5 m above the surface, with the string taut and passing over the pulley.

If the system is then released, taking $g = 10\,\text{m s}^{-2}$, find: (a) the acceleration of the system while the string remains taut; (b) the time taken for X to reach the surface; (c) the tension in the string before X reaches the surface; (d) the time that elapses after X reaches the surface until the string again becomes taut. (Assume that Y never reaches the pulley.)

SOLUTION

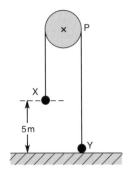

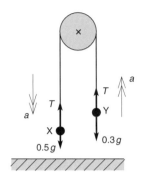

Equation of motion for X
$0.5g - T = 0.5a.$

Equation of motion for Y
$T - 0.3g = 0.3a.$

Solving the two equations we get $\underline{a = 2.5}$ and $\underline{T = 3.75}$.

To find the speed of the system as X reaches the ground:

$u = 0$ Using $v^2 = u^2 + 2as$ Using $v = u + at$
$s = 5$ $v^2 = 0 + 2(2.5)(5)$ $5 = 0 + (2.5)t$
$a = 2.5$ $\underline{v = 5}.$ $\underline{t = 2}.$

To find the time during which the string is slack:
$u = 5$ Using $v = u + at$
$v = 0$ $0 = 5 - gt$
$a = -g.$ $\underline{t = \frac{1}{2}}.$

Thus the total time for which the string is slack is 1 s.

(a) While the string is taut the acceleration = $\underline{\underline{2.5\ \text{m s}^{-2}}}$.
(b) The time taken for X to reach the surface = $\underline{\underline{2\ \text{s}}}$.
(c) The tension in the string = $\underline{3.75\ \text{N}}$.
(d) The time for which the string is slack = $\underline{\underline{1\ \text{s}}}$.

EXAMPLE

5

Two particles P and Q, masses 0.8 kg and 0.6 kg respectively, are attached to the ends of a light, inextensible string, which passes over a smooth pulley fixed at the top of a smooth wedge with a slope of 30°, as shown in the diagram. The string is taut and passes over the pulley with P on the wedge down a line of greatest slope and Q held below the pulley at a height of 6.3 m above the ground.

If the system is then released, find: (a) the acceleration of the system while the string remains taut; (b) the tension in the string before Q reaches the ground; (c) the total distance that P moves up the wedge, assuming it does not reach the pulley.

SOLUTION

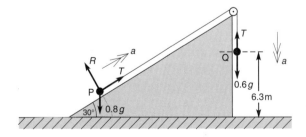

Equation of motion for P
$T - 0.8g \sin 30° = 0.8a.$

Equation of motion for Q
$0.6g - T = 0.6a.$

Solving the two equations we get $\underline{a = 1.4}$ and $\underline{T = 5.04}$.

To find the speed of the system as Q reaches the ground:

$u = 0$
$s = 6.3$
$a = 1.4.$

Using $v^2 = u^2 + 2as$
$v^2 = 0 + 2(1.4)(6.3)$
$\underline{v = 4.2}.$

To find the distance moved by P up the plane when the string is slack:

$u = 4.2$
$v = 0$
$a = -g \sin 30°.$

Using $v^2 = u^2 + 2as$
$0 = 4.2^2 - 9.8s$
$\underline{s = 1.8}.$

Thus the total distance moved by $P = 6.3 + 1.8 = 8.1$ m.

(a) While the string is taut the acceleration $= \underline{1.4 \, \text{m s}^{-2}}$.
(b) The tension in the string $= \underline{5.04 \, \text{N}}$.
(c) The total distance that P moves up the plane $= \underline{8.1 \, \text{m}}$.

EXAMPLE

6

Two particles P and Q, masses 0.4 kg and 0.3 kg respectively, are attached to the ends of a light, inextensible string, which passes over a smooth pulley fixed at the edge of a *rough*, horizontal surface, the coefficient of friction being $\frac{1}{4}$. P lies on the rough surface at a distance of 13 m from the pulley. The string is taut and passes over the pulley, and Q is held beneath the pulley at a height of 5.6 m above the floor when the system is released.

Find: (a) the acceleration of the system while the string remains taut; (b) the tension in the string before it becomes slack; (c) the distance from the pulley of P when it comes to rest.

SOLUTION

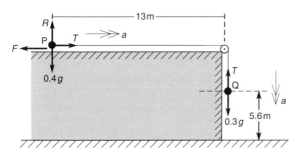

Equation of motion for P
$T - F = 0.4a.$

Equation of motion for Q
$0.3g - T = 0.3a.$

Resolve vertically for P
$R = 0.4g.$

Limiting friction
$F = \mu R = 0.1g.$

Solving the four equations we get $\underline{a = 2.8}$ and $\underline{T = 2.1}$.

To find the speed of the system as Q reaches the ground:

$u = 0$ Using $v^2 = u^2 + 2as$

$s = 5.6$ $v^2 = 0 + 2(2.8)(5.6)$

$a = 2.8.$ $\underline{v = 5.6.}$

To find the distance moved by P along the table after the string becomes slack:

The only horizontal force now acting on P is the friction force.

F still has the value $\mu R = \frac{1}{4}(0.4g) = 0.1g.$

Using Newton's law

$\qquad F = -0.4a'$

$0.1g = -0.4a' \implies \underline{a' = -2.45}.$

$u = 5.6$ Using $v^2 = u^2 + 2as$

$v = 0$ $0 = 5.6^2 - 4.9s$

$a = -2.45.$ $\underline{s = 6.4.}$

Thus the total distance moved by P $= 5.6 + 6.4 = 12\,\text{m}.$
(a) While the string is taut the acceleration $= \underline{2.8\,\text{m}\,\text{s}^{-2}}.$
(b) The tension in the string $= \underline{2.1\,\text{N}}.$
(c) The distance from the pulley of P when it comes to rest $= \underline{1\,\text{m}}.$

Exercises

1   A lorry of mass 3 tonnes is travelling from rest along a level road. Its engine produces a constant tractive force of 2.5 kN, while the total resistances to its motion are constant and equal to 1.6 kN.

Find: (a) the acceleration of the lorry; (b) the speed of the lorry in $\text{km}\,\text{h}^{-1}$ after 1 min 40 s; (c) the distance travelled in this time.

2   A boy of mass 35 kg stands on a weighing machine, which is in a lift. If the lift ascends with an acceleration of $0.7\,\text{m}\,\text{s}^{-2}$, what will the weighing machine register as the boy's weight?

If the lift now decelerates at $0.7\,\text{m}\,\text{s}^{-2}$ what will the weighing machine now register?

3   A lorry of mass 20 tonnes is ascending a slope inclined at θ to the horizontal, where $\sin\theta = 0.01$. The total resistance to its motion up the slope has a constant value R and the engine of the lorry is exerting a constant tractive force of 10 kN.

If the lorry is accelerating at $0.25\,\text{m}\,\text{s}^{-2}$, find the value of R.

If the tractive force of the engine is now switched off, find the retardation of the lorry, assuming that the resistances stay the same.

4 Two small particles A and B, masses 0.3 kg and 0.4 kg respectively, are connected by a light, inextensible string, which passes over a smooth pulley P, fixed at a height of 15 m above a horizontal floor. The particles are held one on either side of the pulley with the string taut, so that each is 6.3 m above the floor.

If the system is now released from rest, find: (a) the time taken for B to reach the floor; (b) the tension in the string before B hits the floor; (c) the time that elapses before A comes to instantaneous rest, and its depth then below P.

5 Two particles A and B, masses 0.5 kg and 0.9 kg respectively, are connected by a light, inextensible string, which passes over a small smooth pulley P fixed at the top of a smooth plane inclined at θ to the horizontal, where $\tan \theta = 0.75$. The particle A is held on the plane 12.9 m from P, with the string lying down a line of greatest slope. The string is taut and passes over the pulley, and B is held below the pulley at a height of 8.4 m above level ground. The system is then released from rest.

Find: (a) the acceleration of the system; (b) the tension in the string while it is taut; (c) the speed of A when it reaches the pulley.

6 Two particles A and B, masses 0.5 kg and 0.6 kg respectively, are connected by a light, inextensible string, which passes over a small smooth pulley P fixed at the top of a *rough* plane, inclined at θ to the horizontal, where $\tan \theta = 0.75$. The particle A is held on the plane 12 m from P, with the string lying down a line of greatest slope. The string is taut and passes over the pulley, and B is held below the pulley at a height of 8 m above level ground. The system is then released from rest.

Given that μ, the coefficient of friction between the plane and A, is 0.2, find: (a) the acceleration of the system while the string is taut; (b) the tension in the string before B hits the ground.

Investigate whether A ever reaches the pulley.

7 A child's slide can be considered to be made up of two parts, AB and BC, as shown in the diagram.

AB is smooth and inclined at $\sin^{-1}(0.8)$ to the horizontal ground, and the length of the slide from A to B is 2 m. The part from B to C can be considered to be rough, the coefficient of friction being 0.2. The slide is suitably rounded at B so that there is no loss of speed as the child passes through B.

Find: (a) the speed of the child at B; (b) the distance the child moves from B to C before coming to rest.

State the assumptions you are making in your solution.

Chapter 4

Impulse, momentum and kinetic energy

This chapter deals with impulses acting on a body, changing its velocity and hence its kinetic energy.

For a constant force F: impulse = force × time.
It is a vector quantity and measured in newton seconds (N s).

Momentum is defined as: momentum = mass × velocity.
It is a vector quantity and measured in newton seconds (N s).

Kinetic energy is defined as: kinetic energy = $\frac{1}{2}$mass × velocity^2.
It is a scalar quantity and measured in joules (J).

> Impulse = change in momentum.

Examples

EXAMPLE 1

A train of mass 10 tonnes starts from rest on horizontal rails.

Find its speed 1 min after starting, given that the tractive force of the engine is constant and equal to 2.5 kN. Ignore resistances.

SOLUTION

Impulse = force × time

Impulse = 2500×60

$\qquad = \underline{150\,000\,\text{N s}}.$

Impulse = change in momentum

$150\,000 = 10\,000v - 0$

$\qquad v = 15.$

The speed of the train after 1 min = $\underline{15\,\text{m s}^{-1}}$.

EXAMPLE 2

A ball of mass 50 g is travelling horizontally with a speed of 60 m s^{-1} when it hits a vertical wall. It rebounds horizontally with a speed of 40 m s^{-1}.

Find the impulse exerted on the ball by the wall.

SOLUTION

Impulse = change in momentum

$\qquad I = (0.05 \times 40) - (0.05 \times -60)$

$\qquad \underline{I = 5}.$

The impulse exerted by the wall = $\underline{5\,\text{N s}}$.

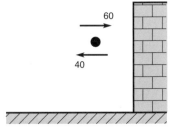

EXAMPLE

3

Two balls A and B, masses 0.5 kg and 0.3 kg respectively, lie on a smooth, level table and are connected by a light, inextensible string, which is initially slack. The ball A now moves away from B with a speed of 4 m s^{-1}. After the string tightens, it remains taut and the two balls then move in the same direction with the same speed V.

Find: (a) the impulse in the string when it tightens; (b) the value of V; (c) the loss in kinetic energy due to the impulse.

SOLUTION

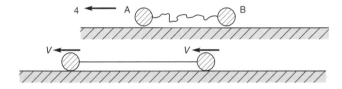

Since the impulses on A and B are equal and opposite, the total momentum must be conserved.

Momentum is conserved	*Impulse equation on B*	*Change in kinetic energy*
$0.5 \times 4 = (0.5 \times V) + (0.3 \times V)$	$I = (0.3 \times 2.5) - 0$	KE before $= \frac{1}{2}(0.5)4^2 = 4$
$V = 2.5.$	$I = 0.75.$	KE after $= \frac{1}{2}(0.8)2.5^2 = 2.5$
		Loss in $KE = 1.5.$

(a) The impulse in the string $= \underline{0.75\,\text{N}\,\text{s}}$.
(b) The value of $\underline{V = 2.5\,\text{m}\,\text{s}^{-1}}$.
(c) The loss in kinetic energy $= \underline{1.5\,\text{J}}$.

EXAMPLE

4

Two small rowing boats A and B are connected by a light rope which is slack. Boat A has a mass of 300 kg, including the rower. Boat B has a mass of 200 kg, including the rower. They start off together in opposite directions with speeds of 6 m s^{-1} and 5 m s^{-1} respectively, until the rope tightens. After the rope tightens, it remains taut and the two boats now move in the same direction with the same speed V.

Find: (a) the impulse in the rope when it tightens; (b) the value of V; (c) the loss in kinetic energy due to the impulse.

SOLUTION

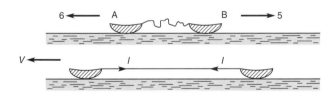

Momentum is conserved	*Impulse equation on A*	*Change in kinetic energy*
$(300 \times 6) + (-200 \times 5) = 500V$	$-I = (300 \times 1.6) - (300 \times 6)$	KE before $= \frac{1}{2}(300)6^2 + \frac{1}{2}(200)5^2$
$V = 1.6.$	$I = 1320.$	KE after $= \frac{1}{2}(500)1.6^2$
		Loss in $KE = 7900 - 640 = \underline{7260}.$

(a) The impulse in the string $= \underline{1320\,\text{N}\,\text{s}}$.
(b) The value of $\underline{V = 1.6\,\text{m}\,\text{s}^{-1}}$.
(c) The loss in kinetic energy $= \underline{7260\,\text{J}}$.

EXAMPLE

5

A pressure hose delivers water horizontally at a rate of 900 kg min^{-1} with a speed of 50 m s^{-1}.

Find the force being exerted on the wall, assuming the water loses all its speed when it hits the wall.

SOLUTION

The impulse on the wall is equal and opposite to the impulse the water receives.

Impulse = force × time   *Change in momentum*

$I = F \times 60$ N s. $(900 \times 50) - 0.$

Hence $60F = 45\,000$

$\underline{F = 750}$.

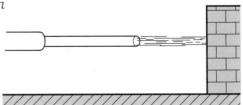

The force on the wall $= \underline{750\,\text{N}}$.

EXAMPLE

6

Three small particles A, B and C, masses 1 kg, 4 kg and 5 kg respectively, lie at rest in a straight line ABC on a smooth table. A is connected to B and B to C by light, inextensible strings, both of which are slack. The particle C is now given a speed of 36 m s^{-1} in the direction ABC away from the others. Subsequently the string BC tightens and then remains taut.

Find: (a) the common speed of B and C after B is brought into motion; (b) the impulse X in BC when it tightens.

Later, the other string AB tightens and then both AB and BC remain taut. Find: (c) the final speed of the system when all the balls are in motion; (d) the impulses Y and Z in BC and AB respectively as AB tightens.

SOLUTION

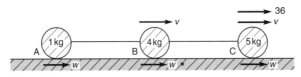

When B is brought into motion:

Momentum is conserved   *Impulse = change in momentum*

$5 \times 36 = 9 \times v$ $X = (4 \times 20) - 0$

$\underline{v = 20}$. $\underline{X = 80}$.

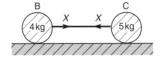

When C is brought into motion:

Momentum is conserved   *Impulse = change in momentum*

$9 \times 20 = 10 \times w$ $Y = (5 \times 20) - (5 \times 18)$

$\underline{w = 18}$. $\underline{Y = 10}$

                                 $Z = (1 \times 18) - 0$

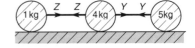

                                 $\underline{Z = 18}$.

(a) The common speed of B and C = $20\,\mathrm{m\,s}^{-1}$.
(b) The first impulse in the string BC = $80\,\mathrm{N\,s}$.
(c) The final common speed = $18\,\mathrm{m\,s}^{-1}$.
(d) The impulses when AB tightens are $18\,\mathrm{N\,s}$ in AB and $10\,\mathrm{N\,s}$ in BC.

EXAMPLE

7

A man uses a rifle to shoot at a target. The rifle has a mass of 4 kg and the bullet has a mass of 15 g. When the rifle is fired, the initial speed of the bullet is $600\,\mathrm{m\,s}^{-1}$.

Find: (a) the initial speed of recoil of the rifle as it is fired; (b) the *total* kinetic energy generated by the firing of the rifle.

The rifle is held against the man's shoulder and he resists the recoil. However, the rifle moves backwards through a horizontal distance of 2.5 cm before coming to rest.

If the force that the man exerts to resist the recoil is assumed to be constant and horizontal, find: (c) the value of this constant force.

SOLUTION

The impulse the bullet receives is equal and opposite to that received by the rifle. Hence the total momentum is conserved.

Conservation of momentum
$4 \times u = 0.015 \times 600$

$\underline{u = 2.25}$.

Change in energy
KE after firing $= \frac{1}{2} \times 4(2.25)^2 + \frac{1}{2} \times 0.015(600)^2 = 2710.125$.

KE before firing $= 0$

Gain in KE $= \underline{2710.125}$.

Motion of the rifle:

$u = 2.25$ Using $\quad v^2 = u^2 + 2as$

$v = 0$ $0 = 2.25^2 + 2a(0.025)$

$s = 0.025$. $\underline{a = -101.25}$.

Equation of motion
$F = ma$

$F = 4 \times 101.25$

$\underline{F = 405}$.

(a) The initial speed of recoil of the rifle $= \underline{2.25 \, \text{m s}^{-1}}$.

(b) The total energy generated by firing the rifle $= \underline{2710.125 \, \text{J}}$.

(c) The force exerted by the man $= \underline{405 \, \text{N}}$.

Exercises

1 A car of mass 1.2 tonnes starts from rest on a level road.

Find the speed of the car 30 s after starting, given that the tractive force of the engine is constant and equal to 0.9 kN. Ignore any resistance to the motion.

2 A ball of mass 30 g falls from rest from a height of 10 m on to a level floor.

If the impulse that the floor gives to the ball results in its speed being halved, find: (a) the height to which the particle now rises; (b) the magnitude of the impulse.

3 Two particles A and B, masses $5m$ and m respectively, lie at rest on a smooth table, and are connected by a slack, light, inextensible string. The particle B is now given a speed of $24 \, \text{m s}^{-1}$ away from A, so that the string subsequently tightens and then remains taut. The particles now travel in the same direction with the same speed.

Find: (a) the common speed of the two particles after the string tightens; (b) the impulse in the string when it tightens.

4 Two small particles A and B, masses $2m$ and $5m$ respectively, are connected by a light, inextensible string. The particles are moving in opposite directions away from each other in the same straight line, each with a speed of $7 \, \text{m s}^{-1}$ on a smooth, horizontal surface. The string subsequently tightens and remains taut, and the two particles move now in the same direction with the same speed.

Find: (a) the common speed after the string tightens; (b) the impulse in the string when it tightens; (c) the consequent loss in kinetic energy.

5 Three particles A, B and C, masses 0.5 kg, 0.3 kg and 0.2 kg respectively, lie in a straight line ABC on a smooth, horizontal surface. Particle A is connected to B and B to C by light, inextensible strings, which are initially slack.

If the particle C is now given a speed of $5 \, \text{m s}^{-1}$ in the direction ABC, away from B, find: (a) the common speed of B and C, assuming the string remains taut; (b) the impulse in the string BC when it tightens; (c) the impulses in BC and AB when the string AB tightens, assuming that both strings then remain taut.

6 A youth uses a rifle to fire at a target. The rifle has a mass of 3 kg and the bullet a mass of 15 g.

If the bullet has an initial horizontal speed of $400\,\mathrm{m\,s^{-1}}$ when it leaves the rifle, find: (a) the initial horizontal speed with which the rifle begins to recoil; (b) the kinetic energy generated by the firing of the rifle.

The rifle is held against the shoulder of the youth, thus providing a constant, horizontal force to resist the recoil. If the rifle moves back a distance of $1.6\,\mathrm{cm}$ find: (c) the value of the constant force needed.

7 Two particles A and B, masses $0.7\,\mathrm{kg}$ and $x\,\mathrm{kg}$, are moving on a smooth, level surface with equal speeds u towards each other, so that there is a direct impact. On impact the particles coalesce into a single particle, which now moves with speed $2u/5$ in the same direction as that of A before the collision.

Find the value of x.

If the loss in kinetic energy due to the collision is $378\,\mathrm{J}$, find the value of u.

8 A ball of mass $0.5\,\mathrm{kg}$ is dropped from a height of $2.5\,\mathrm{m}$ on to a fixed horizontal surface. Each time the ball rebounds, it rises to a height of $0.64 \times$ the depth through which the ball had fallen.

Find the magnitudes of the first two impulses the ball receives from the surface.

9 A string of length $80\,\mathrm{cm}$ connects two particles P and Q of masses $0.6\,\mathrm{kg}$ and $0.1\,\mathrm{kg}$ respectively. Q lies at the edge of a smooth, horizontal table, while P lies on the table at a distance of $40\,\mathrm{cm}$ from the edge, in a direction at right angles to the edge.

If Q is pushed gently over the edge of the table, find: (a) the common speed of the particles after the string tightens; (b) the impulse in the string when it tightens; (c) the loss in kinetic energy due to the string tightening; (d) the time taken for P to reach the edge of the table after it begins to move.

Chapter 5

Work and power

This chapter deals with the notions of work and power.

For a constant force F: work = force × distance.
It is a scalar quantity and measured in joules (J).

Power is the rate of working: power = force × velocity.
It is a scalar quantity and measured in watts (W).

> Work done = change in energy.

Examples

EXAMPLE 1

A car of mass 1 tonne is travelling along a straight road, inclined at an angle θ to the horizontal, where $\sin\theta = 0.28$. The resistance to the motion of the car is constant and of magnitude 200 N.

Find the power being exerted by the engine, in kW, when the car has a speed of $5\,\mathrm{m\,s^{-1}}$ and an acceleration of $0.1\,\mathrm{m\,s^{-2}}$.

SOLUTION

Equation of motion
$$T - R - 1000\,g(0.28) = 1000 \times 0.1$$
$$\underline{T = 3044.}$$

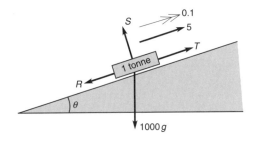

Power = tractive force × velocity
Power = 3044×5
$$= \underline{15\,220.}$$

The power generated by the engine = $\underline{15.22\,\mathrm{kW}}$.

EXAMPLE 2

A car of mass 1.5 tonnes is travelling along a level motorway at a steady speed of $29\,\mathrm{m\,s^{-1}}$. The total resistance to its motion is constant and of magnitude 400 N.

Find: **(a)** the power being generated by the engine.

Using this power, the car now travels at a steady speed up a hill whose inclination to the horizontal is $\sin^{-1}\left(\frac{1}{14}\right)$.

Find: **(b)** the car's speed up the hill, assuming that the resistances remain unaltered.

SOLUTION *Car on the level*

At steady speed $T = R$

$$T = 400.$$

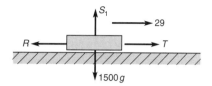

Power = tractive force × velocity

$$= 400 \times 29$$

$$= 11\,600.$$

Car on the hill

At steady speed $T = R + 1500(9.8)(1/14)$

$$T = 1450.$$

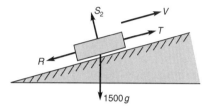

Power = tractive force × velocity

$$11\,600 = 1450 \times V$$

$$V = 8.$$

(a) The power of the engine $= 11.6\,\text{kW}$.

(b) The speed up the hill $= 8\,\text{m s}^{-1}$.

EXAMPLE

3

A car of mass 1 tonne starts from rest on a level road and achieves a speed of $72\,\text{km h}^{-1}$ after it has travelled $400\,\text{m}$.

Neglecting resistances, find the tractive force of the car, assuming it is constant.

SOLUTION We must convert the speed of $72\,\text{km h}^{-1}$ to m s^{-1}; the conversion factor $= 3.6$. Hence $72\,\text{km h}^{-1} = 20\,\text{m s}^{-1}$.

Gain in KE $= \frac{1}{2}(1000)(20^2)$

$$= 200\,000.$$

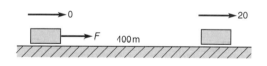

Work done = force × distance

$$- F \times 400$$

$$= 400F.$$

Hence $400F = 200\,000$

$$F = 500.$$

The tractive force of the engine $= 0.5\,\text{kN}$.

EXAMPLE

4

A car of mass 1 tonne is travelling along a level road at a steady speed of $36\,\text{km h}^{-1}$ when the driver sees traffic lights in the distance turn to red. He immediately applies his brakes, producing a constant braking force. For $10\,\text{m}$ the engine is still propelling the car, but after this the driver presses the clutch and so disengages the engine power. The car comes to rest in $40\,\text{m}$, just before the lights.

If the engine was producing a constant tractive force of $160\,\text{N}$, find the retarding force produced by the brakes.

SOLUTION We must convert the speed of $36\,\mathrm{km\,h^{-1}}$ to $\mathrm{m\,s^{-1}}$; the conversion factor $= 3.6$. $36\,\mathrm{km\,h^{-1}} = 10\,\mathrm{m\,s^{-1}}$.

Work done by brakes
$F \times 40$.

Work done by engine
160×10.

Using total work done = change in *KE*

$$40F - 1600 = \tfrac{1}{2}(1000)(10^2)$$
$$40F - 1600 = 50\,000$$
$$F = 1290.$$

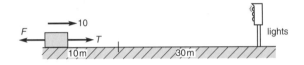

The constant force provided by the brakes $= \underline{1.29\,\mathrm{kN}}$.

EXAMPLE 5

A car of mass 1.6 tonnes starts from rest on a level road and accelerates uniformly to a speed of $54\,\mathrm{km\,h^{-1}}$, covering a distance of $80\,\mathrm{m}$.

If the resistance to the motion of the car is constant and of magnitude $170\,\mathrm{N}$, find: (a) the tractive force of the engine; (b) the power being exerted by the engine when the car's speed is $36\,\mathrm{km\,h^{-1}}$.

SOLUTION We must convert the speed of $54\,\mathrm{km\,h^{-1}}$ to $\mathrm{m\,s^{-1}}$; the conversion factor $= 3.6$. $54\,\mathrm{km\,h^{-1}} = 15\,\mathrm{m\,s^{-1}}$. Similarly $36\,\mathrm{km\,h^{-1}} = 10\,\mathrm{m\,s^{-1}}$.

Work done by forces
$(T - 170) \times 80$.

Change in KE
$\tfrac{1}{2}(1600)(15^2)$.

Using work done = change in *KE*

$$(T - 170) \times 80 = 180\,000$$
$$T = 2420.$$

Using power = tractive force $\times$ velocity

$$= 2420 \times 10$$
$$= \underline{24\,200}.$$

(a) The tractive force of the engine $= \underline{2.42\,\mathrm{kN}}$.
(b) The power exerted at $36\,\mathrm{km\,h^{-1}} = \underline{24.2\,\mathrm{kW}}$.

EXAMPLE 6

A locomotive of mass 25 tonnes is travelling up an incline of $\sin^{-1}(0.01)$ to the horizontal. The resistance to its motion has a constant value of $900\,\mathrm{N}$ and the locomotive is accelerating at $0.2\,\mathrm{m\,s^{-2}}$.

Find: (a) the tractive force of the engine; (b) the power of the engine when the speed is $18\,\mathrm{km\,h^{-1}}$.

If the maximum power that can be exerted by the locomotive is $67\,\mathrm{kW}$, find: (c) the maximum steady speed that the locomotive can achieve up the slope with this power.

SOLUTION We must convert the speed of $18\,\mathrm{km\,h^{-1}}$ to $\mathrm{m\,s^{-1}}$; the conversion factor $= 3.6$. $18\,\mathrm{km\,h^{-1}} = 5\,\mathrm{m\,s^{-1}}$.

Equation of motion up the plane

$$T_1 - R - 25\,000(9.8)(0.01) = 25\,000(0.2)$$

$$T_1 = 900 + 2450 + 5000$$

$$\underline{T_1 = 8350}.$$

Power = tractive force ×velocity

$$\text{Power} = 8350 \times 5$$

$$= \underline{41\,750}$$

Using the maximum power of 67 kW.

Power = tractive force × velocity.

$$67\,000 = T_2 \times v.$$

At steady speed up the plane

$$T_2 = R + 25\,000\,g(0.01)$$

$$\frac{67\,000}{v} = 900 + 2450$$

$$\underline{v = 20}.$$

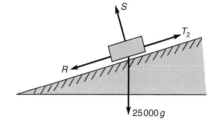

(a) The tractive force of the engine = $\underline{8.35\,\text{kN}}$.

(b) The power generated when the speed is 18 km h^{-1} = $\underline{41.75\,\text{kW}}$.

(c) The velocity when maximum power is used = 20 m s^{-1} = $\underline{72\,\text{km h}^{-1}}$.

Exercises

1 A car of mass 1.8 tonnes starts from rest on a level road and achieves a speed of 54 km h^{-1} after travelling a distance of 50 m.

Neglecting resistances, find the tractive force of the car's engine, assuming it to be constant.

2 A lorry of mass 1.5 tonnes is travelling along a straight road inclined at sin^{-1}(0.1) to the horizontal. The resistance to the motion of the lorry has a constant value of 220 N.

Find the power being generated by the lorry's engine when the speed of the lorry is 10 m s^{-1} and its acceleration is 0.2 m s^{-2}.

3 A car of mass 500 kg is travelling along a level road at a steady speed of 20 m s^{-1}. The total resistance to its motion is constant and of magnitude 380 N.

Find: (a) the power being exerted by the engine of the car.

Using this power the car now ascends a hill whose inclination to the horizontal is sin^{-1}(0.05).

Find: (b) the constant speed with which the car ascends the hill, assuming that the resistances stay the same.

Chapter 5

4 A boy rides his bicycle along a level road. The combined mass of the boy and the bicycle is 100 kg. He starts from rest and accelerates uniformly, reaching a speed of $72\,\text{km h}^{-1}$ in covering a distance of 1 km.

If the resistance to his motion has a constant value of 40 N, find: (a) the horizontal force produced by the boy; (b) the power he exerts when his speed is $27\,\text{km h}^{-1}$.

5 A train of mass 40 tonnes is travelling up a slight incline, the inclination being $\sin^{-1}(0.005)$ to the horizontal. The resistance to its motion has a constant value of 3.84 kN and the train has an acceleration of $0.08\,\text{m s}^{-2}$.

Find: (a) the tractive force of the train; (b) the power of the train when its speed is $45\,\text{km h}^{-1}$.

If the maximum possible power that the train can exert is 116 kW, find: (c) the maximum steady speed with which the train can ascend the hill.

6 A train of mass 200 tonnes is ascending a slight incline at a steady speed of $90\,\text{km h}^{-1}$, the inclination being $\sin^{-1}\left(\frac{1}{196}\right)$ to the horizontal. The total resistance to the motion of the train is constant and of magnitude 20 kN.

(a) Find the power being exerted by the engine.

If the same tractive force continues when the train comes to a level part of the track, find: (b) its acceleration.

Find also (c) the power that is being generated when the train has travelled 2.75 km on the level.

7 The engine of a lorry of mass 5 tonnes can exert a maximum power of 40 kW.

If the resistance to the motion of the lorry is constant and of magnitude 1.5 kN, find the maximum speed in km h^{-1} that the lorry can achieve: (a) on the level; (b) up a hill inclined at $\sin^{-1}\left(\frac{1}{49}\right)$ to the horizontal.

8 The magnitude of the resistance to the motion of a lorry is a constant K newtons per tonne. The lorry has a mass of 2.25 tonnes and is travelling along a straight, level road at a steady speed of $90\,\text{km h}^{-1}$, its engine exerting a power of 11.25 kW.

Show that $K = 200$.

The lorry now ascends a hill inclined at $\sin^{-1}\left(\frac{1}{196}\right)$ to the horizontal with the same power and against the same resistances.

Find the kinetic energy of the lorry when it is travelling at its maximum speed up the hill.

Chapter 6
Projectiles

This chapter deals with projectiles and their trajectories.

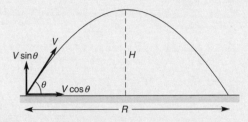

Time of flight $T = (2V \sin \theta)/g$.

The range $= (V^2 \sin 2\theta)/g$.

The greatest height $= (V^2 \sin^2 \theta)/2g$.

The maximum range is when $\theta = 45°$.

The maximum range $= V^2/g$.

The equation of the trajectory: $\quad y = x \tan \theta - \dfrac{gx^2}{2V^2} \sec^2 \theta$.

Examples

EXAMPLE

1

A shell is fired from a point A on level ground with a speed of $245 \, \mathrm{m \, s^{-1}}$ at an angle θ to the horizontal, where $\tan \theta = 0.75$.

Find: (a) the total time that elapses before the shell hits the ground; (b) the greatest height attained by the shell; (c) the range that the shell attains.

SOLUTION

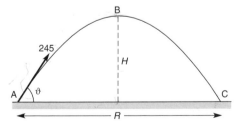

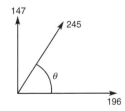

Vertical motion

Motion from A to B:

$u = 147$

$a = -9.8$

$v = 0$.

Horizontal motion

Motion from A to C:

$u = 196$

$a = 0$.

Using $v = u + at$ Using $s = ut$

$\qquad 0 = 147 - 9.8t$ $\qquad R = 196 \times 30$

$\qquad t = \underline{15}.$ $\qquad R = \underline{5880}.$

Using $s = \frac{1}{2}(u + v)t$

$\qquad H = \frac{1}{2}(147 + 0) \times 15$

$\qquad H = \underline{1102.5}.$

(a) The total time of flight $= \underline{\underline{30\,\text{s}}}.$
(b) The greatest height attained $= \underline{1102.5\,\text{m}}.$
(c) The range $= \underline{5.88\,\text{km}}.$

EXAMPLE

2 **A particle is projected from a point A on level ground with an initial speed of $29.4\,\text{m}\,\text{s}^{-1}$ at an angle θ to the horizontal.**

State the value of θ for which a maximum range would be attained.

With this value of θ find: (a) the maximum range; (b) the greatest height attained.

SOLUTION For maximum range $\theta = 45°$.

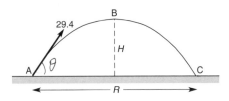

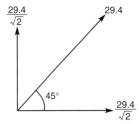

Vertical motion *Horizontal motion*

Motion from A to B: Motion from A to C:

$\qquad u = 29.4/\sqrt{2}$ $\qquad u = 29.4/\sqrt{2}$

$\qquad a = -9.8$ $\qquad a = 0.$

$\qquad v = 0.$

Using $v^2 = u^2 + 2as$

$\qquad 0 = (29.4/\sqrt{2})^2 - 2(9.8)H$

$\qquad \underline{H = 22.05}.$

Using $v = u + at$ Using $s = ut$

$\qquad 0 = 29.4/\sqrt{2} - 9.8t$ $\qquad R = 29.4/\sqrt{2} \times 3\sqrt{2}$

$\qquad \underline{t = 3\sqrt{2}/2}.$ $\qquad \underline{R = 88.2}.$

Hence: (a) the maximum range $= \underline{88.2\,\text{m}}$;
(b) the greatest height attained $= \underline{22.05\,\text{m}}.$

EXAMPLE

3 **A particle is projected into the sea from the top of a vertical cliff 280 m high, with a speed of $140\,\text{m}\,\text{s}^{-1}$ at an angle $\tan^{-1}\left(\frac{4}{3}\right)$ with the _upward_ vertical.**

Find: (a) the greatest height above the top of the cliff attained by the particle; (b) the time taken for the particle to reach the sea; (c) the distance from the base of the cliff when the particle falls into the sea.

SOLUTION

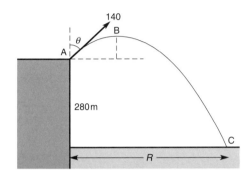

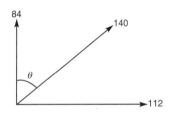

Vertical motion

Motion from A to B:

$$u = 84$$

$$a = -9.8$$

$$v = 0.$$

Using $v^2 = u^2 + 2as$

$$0 = 84^2 - 2(9.8)s$$

$$\underline{s = 360.}$$

Motion from A to C:

Using $s = ut + \frac{1}{2}at^2$

$$-280 = 84t - 4.9t^2$$

$$49t^2 - 840t - 2800 = 0$$

$$7t^2 - 120t - 400 = 0$$

$$(7t + 20)(t - 20) = 0$$

$$\underline{t = 20.}$$

Horizontal motion

Motion from A to C:

$$u = 112$$

$$a = 0.$$

Using $s = ut$

$$R = 112 \times 20$$

$$\underline{R = 2240.}$$

(a) The greatest height above the cliff = 360 m.
(b) The total time of flight = 20 s.
(c) The distance from the base of the cliff = 2.24 km.

EXAMPLE

4

A ball is projected from a point A on level ground with horizontal and vertical components of its velocity equal to $30 \, \text{m s}^{-1}$ and $14.7 \, \text{m s}^{-1}$ respectively. The ball just passes over two vertical walls, each 9.8 m high and at a distance d apart.

By modelling the ball as a particle calculate: (a) the maximum height attained by the ball; (b) the range of the ball; (c) the value of d.

What assumption are you making in the solution?

Chapter 6

SOLUTION

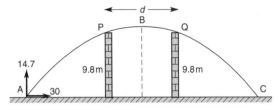

Vertical motion

Motion from A to B:

$$u = 14.7$$
$$a = -9.8$$
$$v = 0.$$

Using $v^2 = u^2 + 2as$

$$0 = (14.7)^2 - 2(9.8)H$$
$$\underline{H = 11.025}.$$

Using $v = u + at$

$$0 = 14.7 - 9.8t$$
$$\underline{t = 1.5}.$$

Motion from A to P:

Using $s = ut + \frac{1}{2}at^2$

$$9.8 = 14.7t - \frac{1}{2}(9.8)t^2$$
$$98 = 147t - 49t^2$$
$$t^2 - 3t + 2 = 0$$
$$(t-1)(t-2) = 0$$
$$\underline{t = 1} \text{ and } \underline{t = 2}.$$

Horizontal motion

Motion from A to C:

$$u = 30$$
$$a = 0.$$

Using $s = ut$

$$R = 30 \times 3$$
$$\underline{R = 90}.$$

Motion from P to Q:

Using $s = ut$

$$d = 30 \times 1$$
$$\underline{d = 30}.$$

Hence: **(a)** the greatest height attained = <u>11.025 m</u>;

(b) the range = <u>90 m</u>;

(c) the value of <u>$d = 30$</u>.

<u>The assumption that must be made is that there is no air resistance.</u>

EXAMPLE

5

A gun fires a shell from a point A on level ground so as to produce a maximum range. The shell just clears a radio tower, which is 21.6 m high and at a horizontal distance of 100 m from A.

By modelling the shell as a particle, find: (a) the time taken for the shell to reach the tower; (b) the initial speed of the shell.

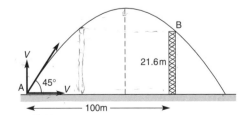

SOLUTION   For maximum range the horizontal and vertical components of the initial velocity are the same. Let each component be V.

Vertical motion	Horizontal motion
Motion from A to B:	Motion from A to B:
$u = V$	$u = V$
$a = -9.8$	$a = 0$
$s = 21.6$.	$s = 100$.

Using $s = ut + \frac{1}{2}at^2$

$$21.6 = Vt - \frac{1}{2}(9.8)t^2.$$

Using $s = ut$

$$100 = Vt.$$

Eliminating Vt from the two equations we get

$$21.6 = 100 - 4.9t^2$$

$$t^2 = 16$$

$$\underline{t = 4} \quad \Rightarrow \quad \underline{V = 25}.$$

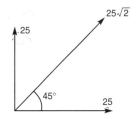

Since each component of the initial velocity is 25, the magnitude of the shell's initial velocity $= 25\sqrt{2}$.

(a) The time taken to the radio tower $= \underline{\underline{4\,\text{s}}}$.

(b) The initial velocity of the shell $= \underline{\underline{25\sqrt{2}\,\text{m s}^{-1}}}$.

EXAMPLE

6   A shell is fired from a point A on level ground with speed $V\,\text{m s}^{-1}$ at an angle θ to the ground. After 10 s the shell is at a height of 1078 m and at a horizontal distance of 1176 m from A.

By modelling the shell as a particle, find: (a) the value of V; (b) the total time of flight of the shell until it explodes on the ground; (c) the speed of the shell when it is travelling at right angles to its initial direction; (d) the time taken to reach this position.

SOLUTION

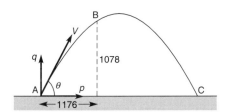

Let the component speeds be p and q as shown.

Vertical motion	Horizontal motion
Motion from A to B:	Motion from A to B:
$u = q$	$u = p$
$a = -9.8$	$a = 0$
$s = 1078$	$s = 1176$
$t = 10$.	$t = 10$.

Using $s = ut + \frac{1}{2}at^2$

$\quad 1078 = 10q - \frac{1}{2}(9.8)100$

$\quad\quad q = 156.8.$

Using $s = ut$

$\quad 1176 = 10p$

$\quad\quad p = 117.6.$

Hence $\quad V^2 = p^2 + q^2$

$\quad\quad\quad \underline{V = 196}.$

From A to C

Using $s = ut + \frac{1}{2}at^2$

$\quad 0 = 156.8t - 4.9t^2$

$\quad\quad \underline{t = 32}.$

When the shell is moving at right angles to the initial direction we have

$W \sin \theta = p$

$\quad W = \dfrac{117.6}{\sin \theta}$

$\quad \underline{W = 147}.$

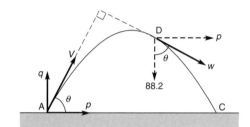

From A to D

$\quad u = 156.8$

$\quad v = -88.2$

$\quad a = -g.$

Using $v = u + at$

$\quad -88.2 = 156.8 - 9.8t$

$\quad\quad \underline{t = 25}.$

(a) $\underline{V = 196\,\text{m s}^{-1}}$.
(b) The total time of flight $= \underline{32\,\text{s}}$.
(c) The shell has a speed $\underline{147\,\text{m s}^{-1}}$ when moving at right angles to its initial direction.
(d) The time taken to reach this position $= \underline{25\,\text{s}}$.

Exercises

1 A particle moves under gravity as a projectile from a point A on level ground. Its initial velocity is $24\frac{1}{2}\,\text{m s}^{-1}$ at an angle $\tan^{-1}(0.75)$ with the horizontal.

Find: (a) the time for the particle to reach the ground; (b) the horizontal range; (c) the greatest height attained.

2 A particle is projected from point A with a speed of $20\,\text{m s}^{-1}$ at an angle θ with the horizontal. It just clears a wall 5.1 m high after 1 s.

Find: (a) the angle θ in degrees; (b) the horizontal distance of the wall from A.

3 A shell is fired from the top of a vertical sea cliff 87.5 m high. It is fired with an initial velocity of $14\,\text{m}\,\text{s}^{-1}$ at $60°$ with the upward vertical.

By modelling the shell as a particle find: (a) the time that elapses until the shell hits the sea; (b) the length of time for which the shell is above the top of the cliff; (c) the greatest height of the shell above the sea.

4 A boy throws a ball with a speed of $39.2\,\text{m}\,\text{s}^{-1}$ at an angle of $60°$ with the vertical. On its descent it just clears a wall 16 m high, lying some distance away on level ground. The ball is thrown from his hand when it is 1.3 m above the ground.

Find: (a) the time the ball takes to reach the wall; (b) the distance of the wall from the boy (answer to three significant figures).

5 A vertical cliff rises 78.4 m from the sea. There is a large gun at the top of the cliff which can only fire shells horizontally.

Modelling the shell as a particle, with what speed should the shell be fired in order to sink a boat which is 1 km out to sea.

6 Two particles P and Q are projected from the same point on level ground at the same instant and with the same speed. P is projected at an angle θ with the horizontal, while Q is projected at an angle θ with the vertical.

Show that: (a) the particles have the same range; (b) the ratio of the greatest heights attained by P and Q is $\tan^2\theta : 1$.

7 A shell is fired from a point A on level ground, so that the maximum range is obtained.

If the shell just clears a pylon 19.6 m high situated at a horizontal distance of 980 m from A, find: (a) the time to reach the pylon; (b) the initial speed of the shell.

8 A shell is fired with speed V from a point O on level ground.

By modelling the shell as a particle, show that, if the range on the horizontal ground is four times the greatest height attained by the shell, it must have been fired originally at $45°$ to the ground.

Given that the greatest height attained is 20 m, find the value of the speed V.

9 An aircraft climbs from a point O on level ground at a steady speed of $45\,\text{m}\,\text{s}^{-1}$ at an angle of $30°$ to the ground. When the aircraft has attained a height of 1510 m, a suitcase drops from the hold.

By modelling the aircraft and the suitcase as particles find: (a) the time taken for the suitcase to reach the ground; (b) its distance from O when it lands on the level ground.

Chapter 7

Impact

This chapter deals with direct collisions of elastic particles and collisions of particles with fixed barriers. It introduces:

Newton's experimental law

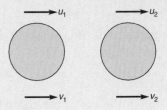

$$v_2 - v_1 = -e(u_2 - u_1)$$

u_1 and u_2 are the speeds of the particles *before* the impact.

v_1 and v_2 are the speeds of the particles *after* the impact.

e is a constant called the 'coefficient of restitution'. Its value depends on the elasticity of the particles.

e has a maximum value of 1 in which case the collision would be said to be 'perfectly elastic'.

$0 \leq e \leq 1$

> Conservation of momentum.
> Newton's experimental law.

Examples

EXAMPLE

1

Two particles A and B, of masses $2m$ and m respectively, are approaching each other with speeds $5u$ and $3u$ respectively. The coefficient of restitution between the particles is $\frac{1}{8}$ and they collide directly.

Find: (a) the speeds of A and B after the impact; (b) the loss in kinetic energy due to the collision; (c) the impulse that occurs between the two particles.

SOLUTION

Momentum is conserved

$(2m \times 5u) + (3m \times -u) = 2mp + mq$

$10mu - 3mu = 2mp + mq$

$7u = 2p + q.$

Newton's experimental law

$q - p = -\frac{1}{8}(-3u - 5u)$

$q - p = u.$

Solving these we get: $\underline{p = 2u}$ and $\underline{q = 3u}.$

KE before impact

$= \frac{1}{2}(2m)(25u^2) + \frac{1}{2}(m)(9u^2)$

$= 29.5mu^2.$

KE after impact

$= \frac{1}{2}(2m)(4u^2) + \frac{1}{2}(m)(9u^2)$

$= 8.5mu^2.$

Loss in $KE = \underline{21mu^2}.$

Impulse – change in momentum

$J = m\,3u - (-m\,3u)$

$\underline{J = 6mu}.$

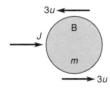

(a) The speeds of A and B after the impact are $\underline{2u \ and \ 3u}.$

(b) The loss in kinetic energy $= \underline{21mu^2}.$

(c) The impulse between the particles $= \underline{6mu}.$

EXAMPLE 2

Two particles A and B, of masses $4m$ and km respectively, are approaching each other so as to make a direct impact. The speed of A is twice that of B, and the coefficient of restitution between the particles is $\frac{1}{3}$.

If A is brought to rest by the impact and B has a speed of $7\,\text{m s}^{-1}$ find: (a) the speed of B before the impact; (b) the value of k; (c) the loss in kinetic energy due to the impact.

SOLUTION

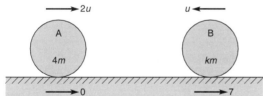

Momentum is conserved

$(4m \times 2u) - (km \times u) = km \times 7$

$u(8 - k) = 7k$

$\underline{k = 4}.$

Newton's experimental law

$7 - 0 = -\frac{1}{3}(-u - 2u)$

$\underline{u = 7}.$

KE before impact

$= \frac{1}{2}(4m)(14^2) + \frac{1}{2}(4m)(7^2)$

$= 490m.$

KE after impact

$= \frac{1}{2}(4m)(7^2)$

$= 98m.$

Loss in $KE = \underline{392m}.$

(a) The speed of B before the impact $= \underline{7\,\text{m s}^{-1}}.$

(b) The value of $\underline{k = 4}.$

(c) The loss in kinetic energy $= \underline{392m}.$

EXAMPLE

3

Three particles A, B and C, of masses 3 kg, 2 kg and 5 kg respectively, lie in a straight line in that order on a smooth, horizontal surface. The coefficient of restitution is $\frac{1}{6}$ throughout. Initially B and C are at rest and A moves at $60\,\mathrm{m\,s}^{-1}$ so as to impinge directly with the particle B.

If subsequently B impinges directly with C, find: (a) the speeds of A and B after the first impact; (b) the speeds of A, B and C after the second impact.

SOLUTION

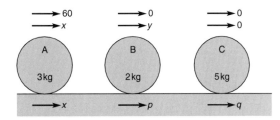

Considering the first collision:

Momentum is conserved

$60 \times 3 = 3x + 2y$

$\quad 180 = 3x + 2y.$

Newton's experimental law

$y - x = -\frac{1}{6}(0 - 60)$

$y - x = 10.$

Solving these two equations we get: $\underline{x = 32}$ and $\underline{y = 42}$.

Considering the second collision:

Momentum is conserved

$2y = 2p + 5q.$

Newton's experimental law

$q - p = -\frac{1}{6}(0 - y)$

$q - p = 7.$

Solving these two equations we get: $\underline{p = 7}$ and $\underline{q = 14}$.

(a) The speeds of A and B after the first impact are $\underline{32\,\mathrm{m\,s}^{-1}\text{ and }42\,\mathrm{m\,s}^{-1}}$.

(b) The speeds of A, B and C after the second impact are $\underline{\underline{32\,\mathrm{m\,s}^{-1},\ 7\,\mathrm{m\,s}^{-1}\text{ and }14\,\mathrm{m\,s}^{-1}}}$.

EXAMPLE

4

Three particles A, B and C, of masses $7m$, $14m$ and $10m$ respectively, lie in a straight line in that order on a smooth, horizontal surface. The coefficient of restitution is $\frac{1}{3}$ throughout. Initially B and C are at rest and A is moving with a speed u so as to impinge directly with the particle B. B subsequently impinges directly with C.

(a) Find the speeds of A and B after the first impact; (b) show that after the second impact the speeds of A and B are the same.

SOLUTION

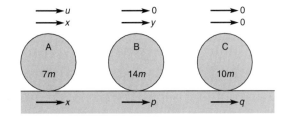

Considering the first collision:

Momentum is conserved

$7mu = 7mx + 14my$

$u = x + 2y.$

Newton's experimental law

$y - x = -\frac{1}{5}(0 - u)$

$5y - 5x = u.$

Solving these two equations we get: $x = u/5$ and $y = 2u/5.$

Considering the second collision:

Momentum is conserved

$14y = 14p + 10q$

$7y = 7p + 5q.$

Newton's experimental law

$q - p = -\frac{1}{5}(0 - y)$

$5q - 5p = y.$

Solving these two equations we get: $p = u/5$ and $q = 7u/25.$

(a) The speeds of A and B after the first impact are $u/5$ and $2u/5.$

(b) After both collisions A and B have the same speed $u/5$, and thus they do not collide again.

EXAMPLE

5

Two particles A and B of equal mass lie on a smooth, horizontal surface in a straight line, which is perpendicular to a fixed, vertical barrier. Initially A and B are at distances $2a$ and a from the barrier. B is at rest, and A is given a speed u so as to collide directly with B. The coefficient of restitution between A and B is $\frac{1}{3}$. Subsequently B collides with the fixed barrier and rebounds in the opposite direction.

If the coefficient of restitution between B and the barrier is $\frac{1}{2}$, find: (a) the speeds of A and B after the first impact; (b) the time taken to this impact.

Show that after the impact of B with the barrier, both B and A have the same speed and find: (c) the time from the start until the particles come to rest; (d) the distance from the barrier when the particles stop.

SOLUTION

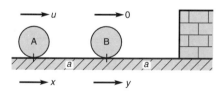

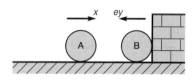

Considering the first collision:

Momentum is conserved

$mu = mx + my$

$u = x + y.$

Newton's experimental law

$y - x = -\frac{1}{3}(0 - u)$

$3y - 3x = u.$

Solving these two equations we get

$$x = \frac{u}{3} \quad \text{and} \quad y = \frac{2u}{3}$$

Considering the collision with the barrier:

Return speed $= e \times$ approach speed

$$= \frac{1}{2} \frac{2u}{3} = \frac{u}{3}.$$

Hence A and B are now moving towards each other with the same speed u.

Time taken to the first collision $= \dfrac{a}{u}$.

Time taken between the first and second impacts $= \dfrac{a}{2u/3} = \dfrac{3a}{2u}$.

The particle A is now at a distance $\frac{1}{2}a$ from the barrier, with B approaching it with the same speed—thus, since they are of equal mass, they will stop when they collide again at a distance $\frac{1}{4}a$ from the barrier.

The further time taken $= \dfrac{\frac{1}{4}a}{u/3} = \dfrac{3a}{4u}$.

The total time taken $= \dfrac{a}{u} + \dfrac{3a}{2u} + \dfrac{3a}{4u} = \dfrac{13a}{4u}$.

(a) The speeds of A and B after the first impact are $\underline{u/3 \text{ and } 2u/3}$.
(b) The time that elapses before the first impact $= \underline{\underline{a/u}}$.
(c) The total time from the start until the particles stop $= \underline{\underline{13a/4u}}$.
(d) The particles came to rest at a distance $\underline{\underline{\frac{1}{4}a}}$ from the barrier.

EXAMPLE

6

Three particles A, B and C, of masses 2 kg, 3 kg and 6 kg respectively, lie in a straight line in that order on a smooth, horizontal surface. Initially B and C are at rest and A is moving with a speed of $5\,\mathrm{m\,s^{-1}}$ so as to impinge directly with the particle B.

If the coefficient of restitution between A and B is $\frac{1}{2}$, find: (a) the speeds of A and B after the first collision.

Subsequently B collides directly with C and the coefficient of restitution between them is e.

Find: (b) the speed of B, in terms of e, after its collision with C.

Given that $e > \frac{1}{4}$, show (c) that there will be a third collision.

SOLUTION

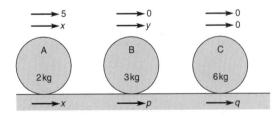

Considering the first collision:

Momentum is conserved	*Newton's experimental law*
$10 = 2x + 3y.$	$y - x = \frac{1}{2}5$
	$2y - 2x = 5.$

Solving these two equations we get: $\underline{x = 0.5}$ and $\underline{y = 3}$.

Considering the second collision:

Momentum is conserved   *Newton's experimental law*

$9 = 3p + 6q$ $q - p = 3e.$

$3 = p + 2q.$

Solving these two equations, we get $\underline{p = 1 - 2e}$ and $\underline{q = 1 + e}$.

If there is to be a third collision, B's speed after its collision with C must be less than A's speed.

B's speed $= 1 - 2e < 0.5$ since $e > \frac{1}{4}$.

$\therefore$ B's speed is less than A's $\Rightarrow$ hence further collision.

(a) The speeds of A and B after the first impact are $\underline{0.5 \, \text{m s}^{-1}}$ and $\underline{3 \, \text{m s}^{-1}}$.
(b) The speed of B after its collision with $C = \underline{1 - 2e}$.
(c) $\underline{\text{Since A's speed is now greater than B's, there must be a third collision.}}$

Exercises

1 Two particles A and B, masses 3 kg and 6 kg, are moving towards each other on a horizontal surface with speeds of $6 \, \text{m s}^{-1}$ and $2 \, \text{m s}^{-1}$ respectively. The coefficient of restitution between them is e.

If A is brought to rest by the direct collision, find: (a) the speed of B after the collision; (b) the value of e.

2 Two particles A and B, masses $3m$ and $2m$, are moving on a smooth, horizontal surface, in opposite directions, with speeds $4u$ and u. The coefficient of restitution between them is $\frac{1}{2}$, and they collide directly.

Find: (a) their speeds after the collision; (b) the magnitude of the impulse that occurs between them.

Subsequently B collides directly with a stationary particle C of mass km and then adheres to it to form one single particle.

Show that, if $k > 5$, a third collision occurs.

3 Three particles A, B and C, masses 6 kg, 4 kg and 3 kg, lie in a straight line in that order on a smooth, horizontal surface. The coefficient of restitution for all impacts is $\frac{1}{6}$. Initially B and C are at rest and A has a speed of $60 \, \text{m s}^{-1}$ so as to collide directly with B. Subsequently B collides with C.

Find: (a) the speeds of A and B after the first collision; (b) the speeds of A, B and C after the second collision.

Deduce that there is a further collision.

Chapter 7

4 Three particles A, B and C, masses 10 kg, 2 kg and 1 kg, lie in a straight line ABC on a smooth, horizontal surface. Initially, C is at rest and A and B are moving towards each other with speeds of $9 \, \text{m s}^{-1}$ and $5 \, \text{m s}^{-1}$ respectively. The coefficient of restitution between A and B is $\frac{2}{7}$, while that between B and C is $\frac{1}{5}$.

Show that after the second collision: (a) A and B are moving with the same speed; (b) the overall loss in kinetic energy is 182 J.

5 Three particles A, B and C, masses 4 kg, 3 kg and 4 kg, lie in a straight line, in that order, on a smooth, horizontal surface. Initially the distance between A and B is the same as the distance between B and C. Particle A is now projected towards B with a speed of $4 \, \text{m s}^{-1}$ so as to collide directly with it. At the same instant C is projected directly towards B with a speed of $1 \, \text{m s}^{-1}$.

Given that the coefficient of restitution is 0.75 throughout, show that, after the second collision, A and B will be moving towards each other with the same speed.

6 Two particles A and B, masses m and $2m$ respectively, lie on a smooth, horizontal surface in a line perpendicular to a fixed, vertical barrier, B being nearer to the barrier. The particle A is given a speed of u so as to make a perfectly elastic collision with B.

Find the speeds of A and B after this impact.

Subsequently B collides with the barrier and then rebounds in the opposite direction.

If the coefficient of restitution between B and the barrier is 0.75, show that B collides with A again.

7 Three particles A, B and C, masses 1 kg, 2 kg and 4 kg, lie in a straight line in that order on a smooth, horizontal surface. Initially B and C are at rest, while A is moving towards B with a speed of $4 \, \text{m s}^{-1}$ so as to make a direct collision with it.

If the coefficient of restitution is $\frac{1}{2}$, show that A is brought to rest by the collision.

Subsequently B collides directly with C and the coefficient of restitution between them is e.

Find, in terms of e, the speed of B after the second collision and deduce that if $e > \frac{1}{2}$, there will be a further collision.

Chapter 8

Motion in a horizontal circle

This chapter deals with bodies moving at constant speeds in horizontal, circular paths.

Any such body requires a radial force which produces a radial acceleration.

Tangential velocity $= r \times$ radial velocity $= Tw$

Radial acceleration $= rw^2 = \dfrac{v^2}{r}$

where r is the radius of the circular path, w and v are the angular and tangential speeds.

> Resolve vertically.
>
> Radial equation of motion.

Examples

EXAMPLE

1

One end A of a light, inelastic string AB of length 90 cm is fixed to a point on a smooth horizontal table. A small particle of mass 100 g is fastened to the other end of the string. The string is pulled taut and the particle is then made to execute constant, horizontal, circular motion on the table with the string remaining taut.

If it takes 3 s to complete one circle, find: (a) the angular speed of the particle; (b) the tension in the string, answering correct to three significant figures.

SOLUTION

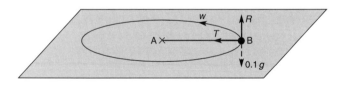

The particle does one circuit in 3 s, i.e. 2π rad in 3 s. Its angular speed is therefore $2\pi/3 \, \text{rad s}^{-1} = \underline{2.09}$.

Radial equation of motion

$T = mrw^2$

$T = 0.1 \times 0.9 \times (2\pi/3)^2$

$T = \underline{0.395}$.

(a) The angular speed of the particle $= \underline{2.09 \, \text{rad s}^{-1}}$.
(b) The tension in the string $= \underline{0.395 \, \text{N}}$.

EXAMPLE

2

A small particle of mass 20 g lies inside a smooth pan with a flat base, which rests on a horizontal table. The pan is circular and 24 cm in diameter, and the particle is rotating round the inner edge such that it does five circuits every second.

Find: (a) the angular speed of the particle; (b) the radial pressure exerted on the particle by the side of the pan.

SOLUTION

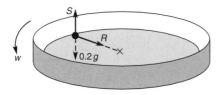

The particle executes five circuits every second.

Hence the angular speed of the particle $= 5 \times 2\pi \, \mathrm{rad \, s}^{-1}$

$$= \underline{31.4}.$$

Radial equation of motion

$$R = mrw^2$$

$$R = 0.02 \times 0.12 \times (10\pi)^2$$

$$R = \underline{2.37}.$$

(a) The angular speed of the particle $= \underline{31.4 \, \mathrm{rad \, s}^{-1}}$.

(b) The radial pressure of the edge of the pan on the particle $= \underline{2.37 \, \mathrm{N}}$.

EXAMPLE

3

A smooth glass bowl of radius 10 cm rests on a horizontal table. The bowl is in the form of a hemisphere, and inside there is a particle of mass 5 g rotating in horizontal circles with an angular speed of $14 \, \mathrm{rad \, s}^{-1}$.

Find: (a) the reaction of the bowl on the particle; (b) the vertical distance of the particle from the top of the bowl.

SOLUTION

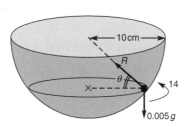

Radial equation of motion

$$R \cos\theta = mrw^2$$

$$R \cos\theta = (0.005)(0.1 \cos\theta)(14^2)$$

$$R = \underline{0.098}.$$

Resolve vertically

$$R \sin\theta = mg$$

$$0.098 \sin\theta = 0.005 \, (9.8)$$

$$\sin\theta = \underline{0.5}.$$

The depth of the particle below the rim $= r \sin \theta$

$$= 10 \times 0.5$$

$$= \underline{5}.$$

(a) The reaction of the bowl on the particle $= \underline{0.098\,\text{N}}$.

(b) The depth of the particle below the top of the bowl $= \underline{5\,\text{cm}}$.

EXAMPLE

4

Two particles A and B, masses m and $3m$, are connected by a light, inextensible string, which passes through a small hole C in a smooth, horizontal table. The particle A moves on the table, describing a horizontal circle with C as its centre and radius a. Its angular speed is w, where $w^2 = 2g/a$. The particle B hangs at rest below the hole C and is supported by a fixed horizontal ledge.

If the string remains taut, find: (a) the tension in the string; (b) the contact force of the ledge on B.

If the angular speed of A is now increased, what is the maximum value it can be given before B begins to rise off the ledge?

SOLUTION

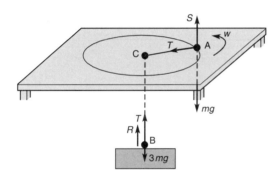

Radial equation of motion for A   *Resolve vertically for B*

$T = mrw^2$ $R + T = 3mg$

$T = ma \times 2g/a$

$T = \underline{2mg}.$ $R = \underline{mg}.$

The maximum value that w can take will occur when R becomes zero.

Hence $T = 3mg$

$$maw^2 = 3mg$$

$$\underline{w^2 = 3g/a}.$$

(a) The tension in the string $= \underline{2mg}$.

(b) The contact force of the ledge $= \underline{mg}$.

(c) The greatest value that w can attain $= \underline{\sqrt{(3g/a)}}$.

EXAMPLE

5

A small bead of mass m is threaded on a light, smooth, inextensible string of length $8a$. The ends of the string are fastened to two fixed points A and B, A being at a vertical distance of 4a above B. The bead is describing horizontal circles with constant speed w and centre B.

If the string remains taut, find: (a) the radius of the circular path described by the bead; (b) the tension in the string; (c) the value of w in terms of a and g; (d) the time for one revolution.

SOLUTION

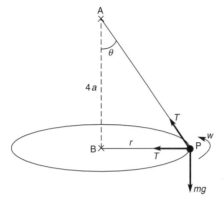

Let the radius of the circle be $r \Rightarrow AP = 8a - r$.

By Pythagoras: $(8a - r)^2 = (4a)^2 + r^2$

$$64a^2 - 16ar + r^2 = 16a^2 + r^2$$

$$\underline{\underline{r = 3a}}.$$

Radial equation of motion

$$T + T\sin\theta = mrw^2$$

$$\tfrac{8}{5}T = m \times 3a \times w^2$$

$$2mg = 3maw^2$$

$$w^2 = \frac{2g}{3a}.$$

Resolve vertically

$$T\cos\theta = mg$$

$$\tfrac{4}{5}T = mg$$

$$T = \tfrac{5}{4}mg.$$

The time for a revolution $= 2\pi/w$

$$= 2\pi\sqrt{(3a/2g)}.$$

(a) The radius of the circle $= \underline{\underline{3a}}$.
(b) The tension in the string $= \underline{\underline{5mg/4}}$.
(c) The value of $w = \underline{\underline{\sqrt{(2g/3a)}}}$.
(d) The periodic time $= \underline{\underline{2\pi\sqrt{(3a/2g)}}}$.

EXAMPLE

6

A particle of mass m is fastened to a point P of a light inextensible string of the length $7a$. The ends of the string are fastened to two fixed points A and B, A being at a vertical distance $5a$ above B. $AP = 4a$, $BP = 3a$ and the particle describes horizontal circles with constant speed w, where $w^2 = 5g/6a$.

If the strings are taut, find: (a) the tensions in the two parts of the string; (b) the minimum value that could be given to w so that such motion could continue.

SOLUTION $r = 4a \sin \theta$

$\underline{r = 12a/5.}$

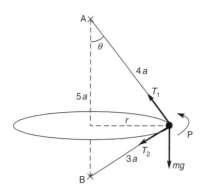

Radial equation of motion

$T_1 \sin \theta + T_2 \cos \theta = mrw^2$

$\tfrac{3}{5} T_1 + \tfrac{4}{5} T_2 = \tfrac{12}{5} maw^2$

$3T_1 + 4T_2 = 10mg.$

Resolve vertically

$T_1 \cos \theta = T_2 \sin \theta + mg$

$\tfrac{4}{5} T_1 - \tfrac{3}{5} T_2 = mg$

$4T_1 - 3T_2 = 5mg.$

Solving these two equations we get: $\underline{T_1 = 2mg}$ and $\underline{T_2 = mg.}$

The least value of w will occur when the string BP loses its tension.

Radial equation of motion

$T_1 \sin \theta = mrw^2.$

Resolve vertically

$T_1 \cos \theta = mg.$

Dividing these two equations

$mg \tan \theta = mrw^2$

$\tfrac{3}{4} g = \tfrac{12}{5} aw^2$

$w^2 = \dfrac{5g}{16a}.$

Hence the minimum value of $\underline{w = \sqrt{(5g/16a)}.}$

(a) The tensions in the two parts of the string are $\underline{2mg}$ and $\underline{mg}$.

(b) The minimum possible $\underline{\underline{w = \sqrt{(5g/16a)}.}}$

EXAMPLE

7

A particle of mass m is attached to one end B of a light, inelastic string of length a. The other end A is fastened to a fixed point above a smooth, horizontal surface. The particle is executing horizontal circles on the smooth surface with constant angular speed w, where $w^2 = 3g/8a$.

If the string is taut and inclined at 60° to the vertical, find: (a) the tension in the string; (b) the normal contact force of the table on the particle.

SOLUTION

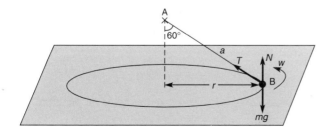

Radial equation of motion

$$T \sin 60° = mrw^2$$

$$T \sin 60° = ma \sin 60° \, w^2$$

$$\underline{T = \tfrac{3}{8}mg.}$$

Resolve vertically

$$T \cos 60° + N = mg$$

$$\tfrac{1}{2}T + N = mg$$

$$\underline{N = \tfrac{13}{16}mg.}$$

(a) The tension in the string $= 3mg/8$.

(b) The contact force of the table on the particle $= 13mg/16$.

EXAMPLE

8

A racing car of mass 0.5 tonnes is travelling at $180 \, \text{km h}^{-1}$ round a circular track whose radius is 400 m.

(a) At what angle should the track be banked so that there will be no tendency for the car to side-slip?

The track is in fact banked at 20°. (b) What sideways frictional force will be needed to prevent side-slipping?

SOLUTION

Radial equation of motion

$$R \sin \theta = \frac{mv^2}{r}.$$

Resolve vertically

$$R \cos \theta = mg.$$

Dividing the equations

$$\tan \theta = \frac{v^2}{gr}$$

$$\tan \theta = \frac{50^2}{(9.8)(400)}$$

$$\underline{\theta = 32.5°.}$$

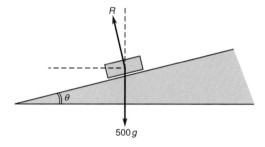

500 g

Radial equation of motion

$$F \cos 20° + R \sin 20° = \frac{mv^2}{r}.$$

Resolve vertically

$$R \cos 20° = mg + F \sin 20°.$$

$$F \cos 20° + \frac{mg}{\cos 20°} \sin 20° + F \frac{\sin^2 20°}{\cos 20°} = \frac{500(50)^2}{400}$$

$$F(\cos^2 20° + \sin^2 20°) + mg \sin 20° = 3125 \cos 20°$$

$$F + 1676 = 2936$$

$$\underline{F = 1260.}$$

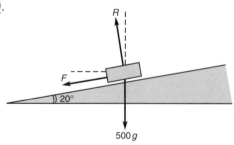

500 g

(a) The racing track should be banked at $\underline{32.5°}$.

(b) The sideways friction force needed $= \underline{1260 \, \text{N}}$.

Exercises

1 A light, inextensible string AB of length 50 cm has its end A fastened to a point on a smooth, horizontal surface. A particle of mass 250 g is attached to the other end B. The string is made taut and then the particle is given an impulse so that it executes constant circular motion, completing 15 circles in 1 min.

Find: (a) the angular speed of the particle; (b) the tension in the string, answering correct to three significant figures.

2 A particle of mass 36 g is travelling round the inside edge of a smooth circular tray resting on a horizontal table. It completes eight circuits in 3 s and the radial force provided by the edge of the tray is 10 N.

Find: (a) the angular speed of the particle; (b) the diameter of the tray, answering to the nearest centimetre.

3 The ends of a light, inextensible string $18a$ long are attached to two fixed points A and B in the same vertical line, B being at a distance $12a$ below A. A small, smooth ring R of mass m is threaded on the string, and the ring revolves in a horizontal circle with constant speed and with the point B as its centre.

Find: (a) the radius of the circle in which the ring rotates; (b) the tension in the string; (c) the period of revolution of the ring.

4 A particle of mass m is fastened to the mid-point C of a light, inextensible string of length $2a$. The ends of the string are fastened to two fixed points A and B, A being vertically above B. The particle at C is executing horizontal circles with constant angular speed w, where $w^2 = 3g/a$. Each portion of the string is taut and inclined at 60° to the vertical.

Find: (a) the tensions in the two parts of the string; (b) the minimum value that can be given to w for such circular motion to continue.

5 A light, inextensible string of length $8a$ is threaded through a small, smooth ring of mass m. The string has one end fixed to a point A on a smooth, horizontal table, while the other end is fastened to a fixed point B, which lies at a distance $4a$ vertically above A. The ring is now projected so as to describe horizontal circles in contact with the table. The string is taut and the angular speed of the ring is constant and of magnitude $\sqrt{(2g/5a)}$.

Find: (a) the radius of the circle in which the ring travels; (b) the tension in the string; (c) the normal contact force of the table on the ring.

6 A particle of mass $\sqrt{2}m$ is fastened to the mid-point of a light, inextensible string of length $2a$. One end of the string is fastened to a fixed point A on a smooth, vertical pole, while the other end of the string is fastened to a small, smooth ring, also of mass $\sqrt{2}m$, which is free to slide on the pole. The particle P is made to execute horizontal circles with constant speed w and such that the angle APB = 90°, with the two parts of the string taut.

Find: (a) the tensions in the two parts of the string; (b) the normal contact force of the pole on the ring; (c) the value of w.

7 A car of mass 1 tonne is travelling round a circular road of radius 500 m at a speed of $162 \, \text{km} \, \text{h}^{-1}$.

At what angle should the road be banked so that there will be no tendency to side-slip?

If in fact the road is only banked at $20°$, calculate the sideways frictional force needed if the car is not to side-slip.

8 A smooth, hollow cone is fixed with its base uppermost and its axis vertical. A particle of mass m is made to rotate in a horizontal circle on the inner surface of the cone.

If the particle is at a height d above the vertex of the cone, prove that its speed v is given by $v^2 = gd$.

Chapter 9

Motion in a vertical circle

This chapter deals with bodies moving under gravity in fixed vertical circles.

Considerations of energy conservation are used.

This brings in the concept of potential energy, which is energy derived by nature of a body's height.

Potential energy $= mgh$

Tangential velocity $= r \times$ radial velocity $= vw$

Radial acceleration $= rw^2 = \dfrac{v^2}{r}$

where r is the radius of the circular path, w and v are the angular and tangential speeds, and h is the height of the body relative to some fixed level.

> Conservation of energy.
> Radial equation of motion.

Examples

EXAMPLE

1

An inelastic string AB of length a has its end A fastened to a fixed horizontal bar. The other end B carries a particle of mass m. When the particle is hanging in equilibrium, it is given a horizontal speed u, perpendicular to the bar, such that it begins to travel in a vertical circle.

Prove that: (a) if $u^2 = 2ag$, the particle comes to instantaneous rest at the level of the bar; (b) if $u^2 = 7ag/2$, the particle leaves its circular path when it is at a vertical height $\frac{1}{2}a$ above the bar.

SOLUTION   We will choose the zero potential energy level to be at the bar.

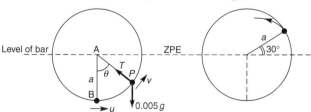

Radial equation of motion

$$T - mg\cos\theta = m\,\frac{v^2}{a}$$

Conservation of energy

At B
$KE = \frac{1}{2}mu^2$
$PE = -mga$

At P
$KE = \frac{1}{2}mv^2$
$PE = -mga\cos\theta$

$$T - mg\cos\theta = m\frac{v^2}{a}$$

$$T - mg\cos\theta = \frac{m}{a}[u^2 - 2ag(1 - \cos\theta)]$$

$$T = \frac{m}{a}[u^2 - 2ag + 3ag\cos\theta].$$

Hence $\frac{1}{2}mu^2 - mga = \frac{1}{2}mv^2 - mga\cos\theta$

$$v^2 = u^2 - 2ag(1 - \cos\theta).$$

If $v = 0$ when $\theta = 90°$, $0 = u^2 - 2ag$

$$\underline{u = \sqrt{(2ag)}.}$$

To find the value of θ when $T = 0$: $0 = 7ag/2 - 2ag + 3ag\cos\theta$

$$0 = 1.5 + 3\cos\theta$$

$$\theta = 120°.$$

Hence the height of the particle above the bar $= a\sin 30°$

$$= \tfrac{1}{2}a.$$

(a) If $u^2 = 2ag$, the particle comes to rest at the level of the bar.

(b) If $u^2 = 7ag/2$, the particle reaches a height $\frac{1}{2}a$ above the bar.

EXAMPLE

2

A particle P of mass m is attached to one end of a light, inelastic string of length a. The other end of the string is fastened to a fixed point A. The particle is hanging in equilibrium below A. A second particle Q, also of mass m, is moving horizontally with a speed V when it collides directly with and adheres to P. The combined particle of mass $2m$ now moves in a vertical circle and just reaches the level of A.

Find: (a) the instantaneous change in tension in the string when the collision occurs; (b) the value of V in terms of a and g.

SOLUTION

We will choose the zero potential energy level to be the level of A.

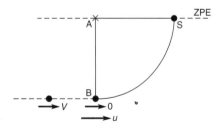

Momentum conserved on collision

$$mV = 2mu$$

$$u = \tfrac{1}{2}V.$$

Radial equation of motion at B

$$T - 2mg = \frac{2mu^2}{a}.$$

Resolve vertically before the impact

$$\underline{T = mg.}$$

Energy is conserved B to S

At B	At S
$KE = \frac{1}{2}2m\,u^2$	$KE = 0$
$PE = -2mga.$	$PE = 0.$

Hence $mu^2 = 2mga$

$$u = \sqrt{(2ag)}.$$

Hence $V = 2\sqrt{(2ag)}$ and $T = 6mg$.

(a) The instantaneous change in tension in the string caused by the collision = $\underline{5mg}$.
(b) The value of $\underline{\underline{V = 2\sqrt{(2ag)}}}$.

EXAMPLE

3

A particle P of mass m is suspended by two light, inextensible strings AP and BP of lengths $4a$ and $3a$ respectively. A and B are fixed points on the same level and at a distance $5a$ apart.

If the particle is hanging in equilibrium, find the tensions in the two strings.

The string BP is now cut so that P now moves in a vertical circle with A as its centre. Find: (a) the speed of the particle when AP is vertical; (b) the tension in the string AP when it is vertical.

SOLUTION   We will choose the zero potential energy level to be the level of A.

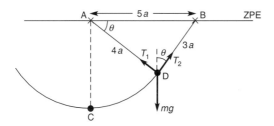

Resolve vertically

$T_1 \sin\theta + T_2 \cos\theta = mg$

$3T_1 + 4T_2 = 5mg.$

Resolve horizontally

$T_1 \cos\theta = T_2 \sin\theta$

$4T_1 = 3T_2.$

Solving these two equations we get: $\underline{T_1 = 3mg/5}$ and $\underline{T_2 = 4mg/5}$.

Energy is conserved D to C

At D	At C
$KE = 0$	$KE = \frac{1}{2}mv^2$
$PE = -4a\sin\theta\,mg.$	$PE = -4mga.$

Radial equation of motion at C

$$T - mg = \frac{mv^2}{4a}.$$

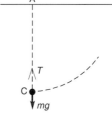

Hence $-4mga\sin\theta = \frac{1}{2}mv^2 - 4mga$

$-\frac{12}{5}mga = \frac{1}{2}mv^2 - 4mga$

$v^2 = \frac{16}{5}ag$ $\implies$ $T = \frac{9}{5}mg.$

(a) The speed of the particle when the string is vertical = $\underline{\sqrt{(16ag/5)}}$.
(b) The tension in the string when it is vertical = $\underline{\underline{9mg/5}}$.

EXAMPLE

4

Two particles A and B, masses m and $\frac{1}{2}m$ respectively, are connected by a light, inextensible string of length πa. The string passes over a smooth, fixed, circular cylinder of radius a, which has its axis horizontal. Initially the particles are at rest with A and B at opposite ends of a horizontal diameter of the cylinder.

Show that, while B remains in contact with the surface of the cylinder,

$$a\dot{\theta}^2 = \tfrac{2}{3}g(2\theta - \sin\theta)$$

where θ is the angle turned through by B and $\dot{\theta}$ is the angular speed.

Find also the tension in the string in this position.

SOLUTION   We will choose the zero potential energy level to be the level of the axis of the cylinder.

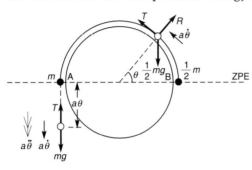

Conservation of energy

Initial energy:

$KE = 0$

$PE = 0.$

Energy later:

$KE = \tfrac{1}{2}m(a\dot{\theta})^2 + \tfrac{1}{2}\left(\tfrac{1}{2}m(a\dot{\theta})^2\right)$

$PE = \tfrac{1}{2}mg\,a\sin\theta - mg\,a\theta.$

Hence $\tfrac{3}{4}m(a\dot{\theta})^2 + \tfrac{1}{2}mga\sin\theta - mga\theta = 0$

i.e. $3a\dot{\theta}^2 = 4g\theta - 2g\sin\theta$

Differentiating: $6a\dot{\theta}\ddot{\theta} = 4g\dot{\theta} - 2g\cos\theta\,\dot{\theta}$

$3a\ddot{\theta} = g(2 - \cos\theta).$

Equation of motion for A

$mg - T = ma\ddot{\theta}$

$$T = \frac{mg}{3}(1 + \cos\theta).$$

The tension in the string $= mg(1 + \cos\theta)/3.$

Exercises

<table>
<tr><td>1</td><td>A particle of mass m lies at rest at the lowest point on the inner surface of a fixed, smooth, hollow sphere of radius a. While in this position the particle is given a horizontal speed V so that it rises up the inner surface of the sphere. The particle leaves the surface when the line joining it to the centre of the sphere makes an angle of 30° above the horizontal through the centre of the sphere.

Find the value of V.</td></tr>
</table>

<table>
<tr><td>2</td><td>A particle P of mass m lies at the top point on the outer surface of a fixed, smooth, solid sphere of radius a, centre O. The particle is now gently displaced.

Find the angle through which OP has turned when the particle leaves the surface of the sphere.</td></tr>
</table>

3 A particle of mass m is fastened to one end B of a light, rigid rod AB of length a. The other end of the rod is smoothly hinged to a fixed point. The rod with the particle attached hangs in equilibrium. Another particle, also of mass m, is travelling horizontally with speed V when it collides directly with the first particle and adheres to it.

Find the speed with which the rod with the combined particle now attached begins to rotate.

Find the value of V if the rod just turns through 180° before coming to rest.

4 A particle P of mass m is freely suspended by two equal, light, inextensible strings PA and PB, each of length a. The points A and B are fixed at the same level and each string makes an angle of 30° with the horizontal when the particle is hanging in equilibrium.

Show that the tension in each string has magnitude mg.

The string PB is now cut so that P begins to rotate in a vertical circle about A as its centre. Find: (a) the change in tension in the string PA when the string PB is cut; (b) the speed of the particle when PA is vertical; (c) the tension in the string when PA is vertical.

5 A particle of mass m is fastened to one end B of a light, inextensible string AB of length $7a/2$, the other end A being fastened to a fixed point. The particle is now held so that the string AB is taut and horizontal and then released.

Find: (a) the speed of the mass when AB has turned through an angle θ; (b) the tension in the string in this position.

When the string is vertical it comes into contact with a small, fixed peg P situated at a distance $3a/2$ vertically below A, so that the particle now begins to rotate in a vertical circle of radius $2a$, with P as its centre.

Show that the tension in the string is instantaneously increased by 50% when it comes into contact with the peg.

Show also that the lower part of the string will now rotate through 120° before it becomes slack.

6 A particle of mass m hangs from a fixed point A by a light, inextensible string of length a. While hanging in equilibrium, the particle is projected horizontally with a speed u, where $u^2 = 7ag/2$, so that it moves in a vertical circle.

Show that: (a) the particle leaves its circular path, i.e. the string becomes slack when it has rotated through 120°; (b) the greatest height attained by the particle above its initial position is $27a/16$.

7 The diagram shows a smooth, solid hemisphere of radius a and centre C, with its plane surface fixed on horizontal ground. A particle P of mass m is released from rest at a point on the surface of the hemisphere such that PC makes an angle β with the upward vertical, where $\cos \beta = 0.75$.

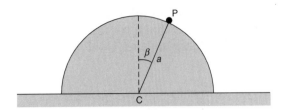

Show that: (a) P leaves the surface of the hemisphere when PC makes an angle of 60° with the upward vertical; (b) P hits the ground with a speed V, where $V^2 = \frac{3}{2}ag$.

8 A particle P slides in a groove ABC, as shown in the diagram. The part from A to B is smooth and in the form of a quarter of a circle of radius 12 m. The part of the groove from B to C is rough, the coefficient of friction being $\frac{1}{4}$. The particle is projected downwards from A with speed u, and subsequently travels along the horizontal part from B to C a distance of 58 m, before coming to rest.

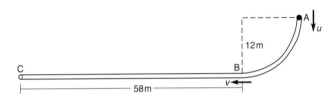

Find: (a) the value of u; (b) the instantaneous percentage change in the normal contact force when the particle passes through B.

9 A smooth, circular wire of radius 20 cm and centre C is fixed in a vertical plane. Two small beads P and Q, each of mass m, are threaded on the wire such that Q lies at the lowest point of the wire while P is held at the highest point. P is now projected along the wire from the highest point with speed u. When it reaches the lowest point, it collides with and adheres to Q, forming a combined bead R of mass $2m$.

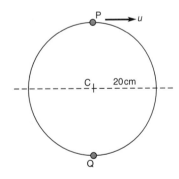

If R subsequently reaches the level of C before coming to instantaneous rest, find the value of u.

Chapter 10

Newton's law of gravitation

Any body of mass m attracts any other body of mass M with a force proportional to the product of the masses and inversely proportional to the square of their distance apart.

$$F = \frac{GMm}{r^2}$$

where G is a constant called the 'gravitational constant' $= 6.67 \times 10^{-11}$, and r is the distance between the centres of the bodies.

If we are considering a satellite orbiting the Earth, we know that at its surface the gravitational force $= mg$.

M = the mass of the Earth $= 6 \times 10^{24}$ kg.

R = the radius of the Earth $= 6.39 \times 10^6$ m.

$$mg = \frac{GMm}{R^2}$$

$$G = \frac{gR^2}{M}$$

$$= \frac{9.8 \times (6.39 \times 10^6)^2}{6 \times 10^{24}}$$

$$\approx 6.67 \times 10^{-11}.$$

If a body of mass m is travelling in a circular orbit around a planet, there must be a force acting on the body towards the centre of the planet $= mrw^2$ (mass × radial acceleration).

Hence $\quad \dfrac{GMm}{r^2} = mrw^2$

$$w^2 = \frac{GM}{r^3} \quad \Longrightarrow \quad v^2 = \frac{GM}{r} \quad \text{(since } v = rw)$$

where r is the distance of the body from the centre of the planet whose mass is M.

Newton's gravitational law:

$$F = \frac{GMm}{r^2}.$$

For a body in a circular orbit:

$$w^2 = \frac{GM}{r^3} \qquad v^2 = \frac{GM}{r}.$$

Examples

EXAMPLE

1

A satellite takes 90 min to complete one circuit of the Earth. Assuming that its orbit is circular and that the gravitational law $F = GMm/r^2$ holds, show that $r^3 = GM/w^2$, where M is the mass of the Earth and w is the angular speed of the satellite.

Given that $M = 6 \times 10^{24}$ kg and the radius of the Earth $= 6400$ km, show that: (a) the satellite is approximately 260 km above the Earth; (b) its speed is approximately 7.75 km s^{-1}.

SOLUTION

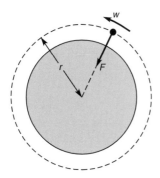

Newton's gravitational law states: $\quad F = \dfrac{GMm}{r^2}$.

The satellite is travelling in a circular orbit and thus must have a radial force acting on it of magnitude mrw^2.

$$mrw^2 = \frac{GMm}{r^2}.$$

Hence

$$r^3 = \frac{GM}{w^2}.$$

The satellite does one circuit in 90 min, i.e. 2π rad in 5400 s.

Hence its angular speed $w = 2\pi/5400 \text{ rad s}^{-1}$.

$$r^3 = \frac{GM}{w^2}$$

$$r^3 = \frac{(6.67 \times 10^{-11}) \times (6 \times 10^{24})}{(\pi/2700)^2}$$

$$r \approx 6\,660\,000 \text{ m}$$

$$r = 6660 \text{ km}.$$

Hence the height of the satellite above the Earth $\approx 6660 - 6400$

$$= \underline{260}.$$

The speed of the satellite $= v = rw = 6660 \times (\pi/2700)$

$$= \underline{7.75}.$$

(a) The satellite is approximately 260 km above the Earth.

(b) Its speed is approximately 7.75 km s^{-1}.

EXAMPLE

2

Using Newton's gravitational law, find the time period of a spacecraft, which is in circular orbit around the Moon at a height of 260 km above its surface.

Assume the Moon to be a sphere of radius 1740 km and mass 7.35×10^{22} kg.

(Take the value of the gravitational constant G as 6.67×10^{-11}.)

SOLUTION

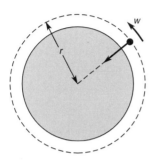

The distance of the spacecraft from the centre of the Moon is r:

$r = 1740 + 260$

$\quad = 2000 \text{ km}$

$\quad = 2 \times 10^6 \text{ m}.$

Newton's gravitational law states: $\quad F = \dfrac{GMm}{r^2}.$

The spacecraft is travelling in a circular orbit, and thus must have a radial force acting on it of magnitude mrw^2.

$$mrw^2 = \frac{GMm}{r^2}.$$

Hence $\quad w^2 = \dfrac{GM}{r^3}$

$$w^2 = \frac{(6.67 \times 10^{-11}) \times (7.35 \times 10^{22})}{(2 \times 10^6)^3}$$

$$w - 7.828 \times 10^{-4} \text{ rad s}^{-1}$$

$$\underline{w = 0.04697 \text{ rad min}^{-1}}.$$

Hence the time for one revolution $= \dfrac{2\pi}{w} = 134 \text{ min}.$

The time for one orbit of the spacecraft $= 134 \text{ min}.$

EXAMPLE

3

A spacecraft is orbiting the Moon, taking 110 min for each circuit.

Assuming that its orbit is circular and that the gravitational law $F = GMm/r^2$ holds, show that $r^3 = GM/w^2$, where M is the mass of the Moon and w is the angular speed of the spacecraft.

Given that the mass of the Moon $M = 7.35 \times 10^{22}$ kg and its radius $= 1740$ km, find:
(a) the height of the spacecraft above the Moon's surface; (b) the speed of the spacecraft relative to the Moon.

SOLUTION

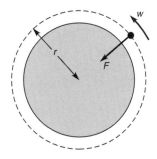

It takes 110 min to complete one circuit, i.e. 110 min for 2π rad.

Hence the angular speed of the spacecraft $= \dfrac{2\pi}{6600}$ rad s^{-1}.

Newton's gravitational law states: $F = \dfrac{GMm}{r^2}$.

The satellite is travelling in a circular orbit and thus must have a radial force acting on it of magnitude mrw^2.

$$mrw^2 = \dfrac{GMm}{r^2}.$$

Hence

$$r^3 = \dfrac{GM}{w^2}$$

$$r^3 = \dfrac{(6.67 \times 10^{-11}) \times (7.35 \times 10^{22})}{(\pi/3300)^2}$$

$$r = 1\,755\,000 \text{ m}$$

$$r = 1755 \text{ km}.$$

Hence the height of the spacecraft above the Moon $= 1755 - 1740$

$$= \underline{15}.$$

The speed of the satellite $= v = rw = 1755 \times (\pi/3300)$

$$= \underline{1.67}.$$

(a) The spacecraft is approximately $\underline{15\text{ km}}$ above the Moon.

(b) Its speed is approximately $\underline{1.7\text{ km s}^{-1}}$.

EXAMPLE

4

A rocket is to be fired vertically from the Earth's surface with speed U.

Assuming that the rocket is subject to Newton's gravitational force $F = \dfrac{GMm}{r^2}$, show that $GM = gR^2$, where R is the radius of the Earth.

Ignoring air resistance, show that the acceleration of the rocket at a distance x from the centre of the Earth is given by $\dfrac{gR^2}{x^2}$.

Taking the radius of the Earth as 6.4×10^6 m, find: (a) an expression for the speed of the rocket at a distance x from the centre of the Earth; (b) the 'escape velocity' required

by the rocket, i.e. the minimum value of U for which the rocket will never return to the Earth's gravitational pull.

SOLUTION   Newton's gravitational law states: $F = \dfrac{GMm}{r^2}$.

At the Earth's surface, we know that $F = mg$.

Hence $mg = \dfrac{GMm}{r^2}$

$GM = gR^2$.

At a distance x from the Earth's centre:

$F = \dfrac{GMm}{x^2} = \dfrac{gR^2 m}{x^2}$

Hence its acceleration $= \dfrac{gR^2}{x^2}$.

The acceleration of the rocket can be written in the form $v\dfrac{dv}{dx}$.

Hence at a distance x from the centre of the Earth:

$$\dfrac{gR^2}{x^2} = -v\dfrac{dv}{dx}$$

$$gR^2 \int \dfrac{1}{x^2}\,dx = -\int v\,dv$$

$$\dfrac{-gR^2}{x} = -\tfrac{1}{2}v^2 + C$$

$\left.\begin{array}{l} v = U \\ x = R \end{array}\right\}$ $\begin{array}{l} -gR = -\tfrac{1}{2}U^2 + C \\ C = \tfrac{1}{2}U^2 - gR \end{array}$

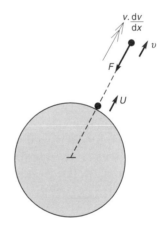

Hence $\underline{v^2 = \dfrac{2gR^2}{x} + U^2 - 2gR.}$

To find the escape velocity, we require v to be positive for all x,

i.e. as $x \to \infty$, $U^2 > 2gR$

$$\underline{U > 11\,200\,\text{m s}^{-1}}.$$

(a) $\underline{\underline{v^2 = \dfrac{2gR^2}{x} + U^2 - 2gR.}}$

(b) The escape velocity $= \underline{\underline{11.2\,\text{km s}^{-1}}}$.

Exercises

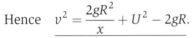

| 1 |

A satellite takes 87 min to complete one orbit of the Earth.

Assuming that its path is circular, show that $r^3 = GM/w^2$ can be obtained from Newton's gravitational law, where M is the mass of the Earth and w is the angular speed of the satellite.

Given that $M = 6 \times 10^{24}$ and the radius of the Earth $= 6400\,\text{km}$, find: (a) the height of the satellite above the Earth's surface; (b) the speed of the satellite.

2 A space probe takes 2 h to complete one circuit of Mercury. Its orbit may be assumed to be circular.

Use Newton's gravitational law to show that $w^2 = GM/r^3$, where M is the mass of Mercury $= 3 \times 10^{23}\,\text{kg}$, and r is the distance of the probe from the centre of Mercury.

Given that the radius of Mercury is 2400 km and $G = 6.67 \times 10^{-11}$, find the height of the probe above the surface of Mercury.

3 A spacecraft is in circular orbit around Mars at a height of 120 km above its surface.

Assuming that the mass of Mars is 6.7×10^{23} and that its radius is 3380 km, find the speed of the probe relative to Mars in $\text{km}\,\text{s}^{-1}$. (Assume that the gravitational constant $G = 6.67 \times 10^{-11}$.)

4 A rocket is to be fired from the Moon's surface with a speed u.

Assuming that the rocket is subject to Newton's gravitational law, $F = GMm/r^2$, show that $GM = gR^2$, where R is the radius of the Moon, M is its mass, and g is the acceleration caused by the Moon's gravity.

Find: (a) an expression for the speed of the rocket when at a distance x from the Moon's centre; (b) the 'escape velocity' required by the rocket. (Take $g = 1.6\,\text{m}\,\text{s}^{-2}$, $G = 6.67 \times 10^{-11}$ and the radius of the Moon $= 1740\,\text{km}$.)

5 One of the minor planets has a radius of 80 km and the same mean density as that of the Earth. A particle is projected upwards from its surface with speed $U\,\text{m}\,\text{s}^{-1}$ so as to 'escape' into space.

The 'escape velocity' must satisfy

$$U^2 > \frac{2GM}{R}$$

where G is the gravitational constant $= 6.67 \times 10^{-11}$, M is the mass of the planet, and R is its radius.

Hence show that, if $U > 140\,\text{m}\,\text{s}^{-1}$, the particle will 'escape' into space. (The radius of the Earth is 6400 km and its mass $6 \times 10^{24}\,\text{kg}$.)

6 A missile is to be fired upwards with speed $U\,\text{m}\,\text{s}^{-1}$ from the surface of Mars.

Model the missile as a particle and assume that the only force acting on it is the gravitational pull of Mars.

If $v\,\mathrm{m\,s^{-1}}$ is the speed of the missile when at a distance $x\,\mathrm{m}$ from the centre of Mars, it must satisfy

$$v^2 = \frac{2GM}{x} + U^2 - \frac{2GM}{R}$$

where G is the gravitational constant $= 6.67 \times 10^{-11}$, M is the mass of Mars, and R is its radius.

Deduce that if the missile is to 'escape' into space, the minimum value of U is approximately $5.2\,\mathrm{km\,s^{-1}}$.

If in fact $U = 5.25\,\mathrm{km\,s^{-1}}$, find the speed of the missile when it is 'free' in space. (Take the radius of Mars to be $3300\,\mathrm{km}$ and its mass $6.7 \times 10^{23}\,\mathrm{kg}$.)

Chapter 11

Elasticity

This chapter deals with the elasticity of strings and springs.

It introduces Hooke's law which states that the tension in an elastic string or spring is proportional to its extension or compression.

$$T = \frac{\lambda x}{a}$$

where T is the tension in the string, a its natural length and x its extension.

The constant λ is called the 'modulus of elasticity' and it is the force required to extend the string to twice its natural length.

It also brings in the concept of elastic energy stored in a string.

Elastic energy $(EE) = \frac{\lambda x^2}{2a}$.

> **Hooke's law:** $T = \frac{\lambda x}{a}$.
>
> **Elastic energy:** $EE = \frac{\lambda x^2}{2a}$.

Examples

EXAMPLE

1

An elastic string of natural length 50 cm and modulus 7 N has one end A fixed to the ceiling of a room. A particle of mass 0.6 kg is attached to the other end B of the string. If the particle rests in equilibrium hanging below A, find the extension of the string.

SOLUTION   Let c be the extension of the string when the particle hangs in equilibrium

In equilibrium

$T_0 = 0.6g$

Hooke's law

$T_0 = \frac{\lambda c}{a}$

$T_0 = \frac{7c}{0.5}$

Hence $0.6g = 14c$

$\underline{c = 0.42}$.

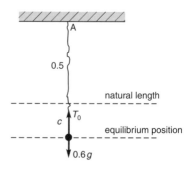

The extension of the string when the particle is in equilibrium = $\underline{42 \text{ cm}}$.

EXAMPLE

2

A particle of mass m is attached to two strings AP and BP. AP is inelastic and of length $3a$. BP is elastic and of natural length $3a$. The other ends A and B of the strings are fastened to two points on a fixed horizontal bar at a distance of $5a$ apart. When the particle hangs in equilibrium, the length of the string BP is $4a$. Find: (a) the tension in the string AP; (b) the tension in the string BP; (c) the modulus of elasticity of the string BP.

SOLUTION

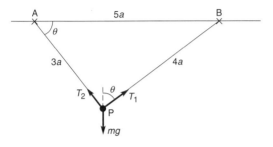

Resolve vertically

$$T_1 \cos \theta + T_2 \sin \theta = mg$$

$$T_1 \tfrac{3}{5} + T_2 \tfrac{4}{5} = mg$$

$$3T_1 + 4T_2 = 5mg.$$

Resolve horizontally

$$T_1 \sin \theta = T_2 \cos \theta$$

$$T_1 \tfrac{4}{5} = T_2 \tfrac{3}{5}$$

$$4T_1 = 3T_2.$$

Hooke's law

$$T_1 = \frac{\lambda a}{3a}$$

$$T_1 = \frac{\lambda}{3}.$$

Solving the first two equations we get: $\quad T_1 = \tfrac{3}{5} mg \quad T_2 = \tfrac{4}{5} mg$.

(a) The tension in the string AP $= \tfrac{4}{5} mg$.

(b) The tension in the string BP $= \tfrac{3}{5} mg$.

(c) The modulus of elasticity $= \tfrac{9}{5} mg$.

EXAMPLE

3

An elastic spring AB of natural length a and modulus $12mg$ has its end A fixed to the ceiling of a room. A particle of mass m is attached to its other end and hangs in equilibrium below A.

Find the extension in the string in this position.

If the particle is now raised to the level of the ceiling and then released, find the greatest depth below A reached by the particle.

SOLUTION

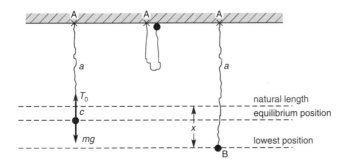

Resolve vertically

$$T_0 = mg.$$

Hence $mg = \dfrac{12mgc}{a}$

$$c = \dfrac{a}{12}.$$

Energy at A

$KE = 0$

$PE = 0$

$EE = 0.$

Hooke's law

$$T_0 = \dfrac{\lambda c}{a}$$

$$T_0 = \dfrac{12mgc}{a}.$$

Energy at B

$KE = 0$

$PE = -mg(a + x)$

$EE = \dfrac{12mgx^2}{2a}.$

Hence $\dfrac{12mgx^2}{2a} = mg(a + x)$

$$6x^2 = ax + a^2$$

$$6x^2 - ax - a^2 = 0$$

$$(3x + a)(2x - a) = 0$$

$$x = \tfrac{1}{2}a.$$

The extension of the string when the particle is in equilibrium $= \dfrac{a}{12}.$

The particle drops a distance $\tfrac{3}{2}a$ before it comes to instantaneous rest.

EXAMPLE

4

A locomotive of mass 216 tonnes is travelling at $1.8\,\mathrm{km\,h^{-1}}$ when it hits two spring-controlled buffers. The two buffers are compressed a distance of $30\,\mathrm{cm}$ before the locomotive is brought to rest.

What is the thrust in each buffer when at this maximum compression?

SOLUTION

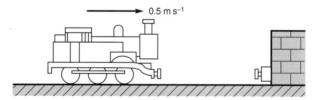

Kinetic energy lost by locomotive

$KE = \tfrac{1}{2}mv^2$

$\quad = \tfrac{1}{2}(216\,000)(0.5^2)$

$\quad = 27\,000.$

Elastic energy gained by buffers

$EE = \dfrac{\lambda x^2}{2a}$

$\quad = \dfrac{\lambda(0.3^2)}{2a}$

$\quad = 0.045\left(\dfrac{\lambda}{a}\right).$

Hence $27\,000 = 0.045\left(\dfrac{\lambda}{a}\right)$

$\dfrac{\lambda}{a} = 6 \times 10^5.$

The total tension in the buffers at full compression is given by

$$T = \frac{\lambda}{a}x$$

$$= 600\,000 \times 0.3$$

$$= 180\,000.$$

This value is shared between the two buffers. Hence each buffer has a tension of 90 000 N.

The thrust in each buffer when at maximum compression = <u>90 kN</u>.

EXAMPLE

5

A particle of mass 0.3 kg is attached to one end A of a light spring of natural length 32 cm and modulus 4 N. The other end B of the spring is fastened to a fixed point on a *rough*, horizontal table, the coefficient of friction being 0.25. The particle is now pulled along the table until the spring's length is 40 cm and then released.

Taking $g = 10\,\text{m s}^{-2}$, show that the particle will travel 4 cm before coming to rest.

SOLUTION

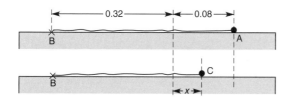

Energy at B

$KE = 0$

$EE = \dfrac{\lambda x^2}{2a}$

$\quad = \dfrac{4(0.08)^2}{0.64}$

$\quad = 0.04.$

Energy at C

$KE = 0$

$EE = \dfrac{\lambda x^2}{2a}$

$\quad = \dfrac{x^2}{0.64}$

$\quad = 6.25x^2.$

The loss in elastic energy = work done by friction.

Friction is limiting (particle is in motion) $= \mu mg$.

Hence the work done by the friction force = force × distance

$$= \mu mg \times (0.08 - x)$$

$$= \tfrac{1}{4}(0.3)(10)(0.08 - x)$$

$$= 0.75(0.08 - x).$$

Hence $\qquad 0.04 - 6.25x^2 = 0.75(0.08 - x)$

$$0.04 - 6.25x^2 = 0.06 - 0.75x$$

$$6.25x^2 - 7.5x + 0.02 = 0$$

Solving this equation: $\quad x = \underline{0.04}.$

<u>The particle travels 4 cm before coming to rest.</u>

EXAMPLE

6

A particle of mass m has two identical elastic strings attached to it. Both strings are of natural length $4a$ and modulus kmg, where k is a constant. The free ends of the strings are now fastened to fixed points A and B at the same horizontal level and at a distance $8a$ apart. The particle is now held at the mid-point C of AB, both strings being at their natural lengths, and then released. The particle drops a distance of $3a$ before coming to instantaneous rest.

By energy considerations find the value of the constants k.

SOLUTION

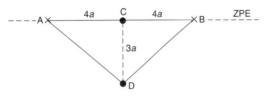

Since the particle drops a distance $3a$, it follows that when it is at its lowest point both strings will now be of length $5a$ and therefore will be extended by a distance a.

Energy at C	*Energy at D*
$KE = 0$	$KE = 0$
$PE = 0$	$PE = -mg(3a)$
$EE = 0.$	$EE = \dfrac{kmga^2}{8a} \times 2.$

Hence $\dfrac{kmga}{4} = 3mga.$

$$\underline{k = 12}.$$

The constant k has the value $\underline{\underline{12}}$.

EXAMPLE

7

A particle of mass m is fastened to one end of an elastic spring of natural length a and modulus $4mg$. The other end of the spring is fastened to a fixed point A on a *rough*, horizontal table. The coefficient of friction is $\frac{1}{2}$. The particle is held with the spring compressed to a length $\frac{1}{2}a$ and then released.

Find: (a) the length of the spring when the particle comes to instantaneous rest; (b) the speed of the particle when the spring is at its natural length.

SOLUTION

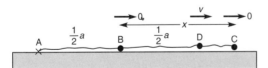

Friction is limiting $\Longrightarrow F = \mu R = \frac{1}{2}mg.$

Initially	*When at rest*
$KE = 0$	$KE = 0$
$EE = \dfrac{4mg}{2a}\left(\tfrac{1}{2}a\right)^2.$	$EE = \dfrac{4mg}{2a}\left(x - \tfrac{1}{2}a\right)^2.$

Work done by friction = change in energy B–C

$\frac{1}{2}mgx = \frac{1}{2}mga - 2mg\left(x - \frac{1}{2}a\right)^2 / a$

$\frac{1}{2}mgx = \frac{1}{2}mga - 2mgx^2/a + 2mgx - \frac{1}{2}mga$

$\frac{1}{2} = -2x/a + 2$

$\underline{x = \frac{3}{4}a}.$

At natural length

$KE = \frac{1}{2}mv^2$

$EE = 0.$

Work done by friction = change in energy B–D

$\frac{1}{2}mg\left(\frac{1}{2}a\right) = \frac{1}{2}mga - \frac{1}{2}mv^2$

$\underline{v = \sqrt{\left(\frac{1}{2}ag\right)}}.$

(a) The length of the spring when the particle first comes to rest $= \underline{\frac{3}{4}a}$.

(b) The speed of the particle when the spring is at its natural length $= \underline{\sqrt{\left(\frac{1}{2}ag\right)}}$.

EXAMPLE

8

A particle of mass m is fastened to one end of an elastic string of natural length a and modulus $40mg$. The other end of the string is fastened to the ceiling of a room.

If the particle is held at the ceiling and then released, find the extension of the string when the mass first comes to instantaneous rest.

Find also the speed of the mass as it passes through: (a) its natural length position; (b) its equilibrium position.

SOLUTION

Considering the energies of the system:

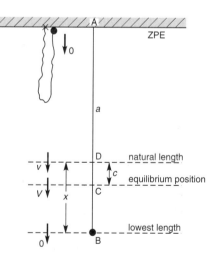

At the ceiling	*At the bottom*
$KE = 0$	$KE = 0$
$PE = 0$	$E = -mg(a+x)$
$EE = 0.$	$EE = \dfrac{\lambda x^2}{2a} = \dfrac{20mgx^2}{a}$

Energy is conserved A–B

$\dfrac{20mgx^2}{a} = mg(a+x)$

$20x^2 - ax - a^2 = 0$

$(5x + a)(4x - a) = 0$

$\underline{x = \frac{1}{4}a}.$

In equilibrium $T_0 = mg$. By Hooke's law $T_0 = 40mgc/a$.

$40gmc/a = mg \implies c = a/40.$

At natural length	*At the equilibrium position*
$KE = \frac{1}{2}mv^2$	$KE = \frac{1}{2}mV^2$
$PE = -mga$	$PE = -mg(41a/40)$
$EE = 0.$	$EE = 40mg/2a\,(a/40)^2 = mga/80.$

 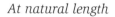

Energy is conserved A–D

$$mga = \tfrac{1}{2}mv^2$$

$$\underline{v = \sqrt{(2ag)}.}$$

Energy is conserved A–C

$$\tfrac{1}{2}mV^2 + mga/80 = 41mga/40$$

$$\underline{V = \sqrt{(81ag/40)}.}$$

(a) The speed when at its natural length position $= \sqrt{(2ag)}$.

(b) The speed when at its equilibrium position $= \underline{\underline{\sqrt{(81ag/40)}}}$.

Exercises

1 An elastic string of natural length 20 cm has one end fixed, and in particle of mass 0.5 kg is attached to its other end and hangs in equilibrium.

If the string is now 25 cm long, find its modulus of elasticity.

2 A particle P of mass m is suspended by two light strings AP and BP. AP is inelastic and 0.9 m long. BP is elastic and of natural length 1 m. A and B are fixed at the same horizontal level and 1.5 m apart. The particle hangs in equilibrium below this level, and the elastic string is now stretched to a length of 1.2 m.

Find: (a) the tensions in the strings; (b) the modulus of elasticity of the elastic string.

3 An elastic spring AB of natural length a and modulus $40mg$ has its end A fixed to the ceiling of a room. A particle of mass m is attached to the other end and hangs in equilibrium.

Find: (a) the extension of the spring in this position.

If the particle is now raised to the level of the ceiling and then released, find: (b) the greatest depth below the ceiling attained by the particle.

4 A train of mass 24.3 tonnes is travelling at 2 km h^{-1} when it hits two spring-controlled buffers. The train is brought to rest when the buffers have been compressed a distance of 50 cm.

What is the force being exerted by each of the buffers when they are at maximum compression?

5 A particle of mass 200 g is attached to one end A of a light, elastic spring of natural length 50 cm and modulus 2 N. The other end B of the spring is fastened to a fixed point on a rough horizontal table, the coefficient of friction being 0.5. The particle is now pulled along the table until the spring is 80 cm long and then released.

Taking $g = 10\,\mathrm{m\,s}^{-2}$, find the distance travelled by the particle before it comes to rest.

6   A particle of mass 2 kg has two identical elastic strings of natural length 50 cm and modulus pg, where p is a constant, attached to it. The free ends of the strings are now fastened to two fixed points A and B, at the same horizontal level and at a distance 1 m apart. The particle is now held at the mid-point of AB, so that both strings are at their natural length and then released.

If the particle now drops 1.2 m before coming to instantaneous rest, find the value of the constant p.

7   A light, elastic string AB of natural length a and modulus $12mg$ has its end A fastened to the ceiling of a room and has a particle of mass m fastened to the other end B. Find the extension of the string when the particle hangs in equilibrium.

If the particle is now pulled down until the extension in the string is $\frac{1}{2}a$ and then released, find: (a) the speed of the particle as it passes through the equilibrium position; (b) the speed of the particle as it passes through the natural length position.

Show that the particle will just reach the level of the ceiling when it first comes to instantaneous rest.

8   A spider S of mass m suspends itself from the ceiling of a room by an *elastic* thread of natural length a and modulus $\frac{1}{2}mg$.

Show that as it hangs in equilibrium the string is of length $3a$.

Another spider P also of mass m is suspended from the same ceiling by an *inelastic* thread of length $3a$.

Find the ratio of the work done by S to that done by P when both spiders climb to the ceiling.

Chapter 12

Simple harmonic motion

A body performs simple harmonic motion (SHM) if its acceleration is proportional to its displacement from some fixed point and is always directed to that fixed point.

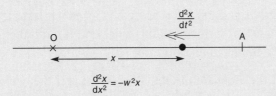

$$\frac{d^2x}{dx^2} = -w^2x$$

where w is a constant.

The body will oscillate between two fixed points A and A′.

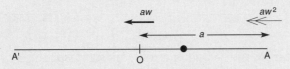

The maximum speed of the body is aw and will occur at O.

The maximum acceleration of the body is aw^2 and will occur at A and A′.

The amplitude a of the motion is the distance OA.

The periodic time T is the time taken to travel from A and back to A, i.e. the time taken to cover a distance of $4a$.

SHM equation:	$\dfrac{d^2x}{dx^2} = -w^2\,x.$
Periodic time:	$T = \dfrac{2\pi}{w}.$
Speed of particle:	$v^2 = w^2(a^2 - x^2).$
Displacement from O:	$x = a\sin wt.$
Time taken from O:	$t = \dfrac{1}{w}\sin^{-1}\left(\dfrac{x}{a}\right).$
Maximum speed:	$V = aw.$
Maximum force:	$F = maw^2.$

Examples

EXAMPLE

1

A particle of mass m is attached to one end of a light, elastic spring of natural length $3a$ and modulus $6mg$. The free end of the spring is fixed to a point on a smooth, horizontal table. The particle is now pulled along the table until the spring is $4a$ long and then released.

Show that the subsequent motion is SHM and find: (a) the maximum speed of the particle; (b) the maximum acceleration of the particle; (c) the time period of the SHM motion.

SOLUTION

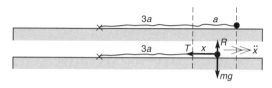

Equation of motion

$$T = -m\ddot{x}.$$

Hooke's law

$$T = \frac{6mg\,x}{3a}.$$

Hence $\quad \dfrac{2mgx}{a} = -m\ddot{x}$

$$\ddot{x} = -\frac{2g}{a}x \qquad \text{i.e. SHM with } w^2 = \frac{2g}{a}.$$

The maximum speed $= aw$

$$= a\sqrt{(2g/a)}$$
$$= \sqrt{(2ag)}.$$

The maximum acceleration $= aw^2$

$$= a\,(2g/a)$$
$$= 2g.$$

The periodic time $= \dfrac{2\pi}{w}$

$$= 2\pi\sqrt{(a/2g)}.$$
$$= \pi\sqrt{(2a/g)}.$$

(a) The maximum speed $= \sqrt{(2ag)}$.
(b) The maximum acceleration $= 2g$.
(c) The periodic time $= \pi\sqrt{(2a/g)}$.

EXAMPLE

2

A particle of mass m is executing SHM between two points A and A$'$, 12 cm apart. It takes 3 s for the particle to travel from A to A$'$.

Find: (a) the amplitude of the motion; (b) the time period of the motion; (c) the maximum speed during its motion; (d) the time taken to move from A to a point B, 3 cm from A$'$.

SOLUTION

3cm		3cm		6cm	
A$'$		B		C	A

The time from A to A$'$ is 3 s. Thus the full time period is 6 s.

The amplitude $a = \frac{1}{2}AA' = 6\,\text{cm} = 0.06\,\text{m}$.

The time period $= \dfrac{2\pi}{w}$

$$6 = \dfrac{2\pi}{w}.$$

Hence $w = \dfrac{\pi}{3}.$

The maximum speed $= aw$

$$= 0.06 \times \dfrac{\pi}{3}$$

$$= 0.02\pi.$$

The time taken from A to C $= \frac{1}{4}T = 1\frac{1}{2}$ s.

The time taken from C to B can be found using the formula

$$t = \dfrac{1}{w}\sin^{-1}\left(\dfrac{x}{a}\right)$$

$$= \dfrac{3}{\pi}\left[\sin^{-1}\dfrac{0.03}{0.06}\right]$$

$$= \dfrac{3}{\pi}\left[\sin^{-1}\tfrac{1}{2}\right]$$

$$= \dfrac{3}{\pi} \times \dfrac{\pi}{6}$$

$$= 0.5\,\text{s}.$$

Hence the time from A to B $= 1\frac{1}{2} + \frac{1}{2} = 2$ s.

(a) The amplitude of the SHM $= \underline{6\,\text{cm}}$.
(b) The periodic time $= \underline{\underline{6\,\text{s}}}$.
(c) The greatest speed $= \underline{\underline{0.02\pi\,\text{m s}^{-1}}}$.
(d) The time taken to travel from A to B $= \underline{\underline{2\,\text{s}}}$.

EXAMPLE

3

A particle P is executing SHM between two points A and B. The point C is the centre of the oscillation. It is known that the speed of the particle is $4\,\text{m s}^{-1}$ when it is 3 m from C and $3\,\text{m s}^{-1}$ when it is 4 m from C.

Find: (a) the amplitude of the motion; (b) the value of w; (c) the maximum speed during its motion; (d) the periodic time.

SOLUTION

Using the formula $v^2 = w^2(a^2 - x^2)$

$\left.\begin{array}{l} v = 4 \\ x = 3 \end{array}\right\}$ $\qquad 16 = w^2(a^2 - 9)$

$\left.\begin{array}{l} v = 3 \\ x = 4 \end{array}\right\}$ $\qquad 9 = w^2(a^2 - 16).$

By dividing these equations:

$$\frac{16}{9} = \frac{a^2 - 9}{a^2 - 16}$$

$$16(a^2 - 16) = 9(a^2 - 9)$$

$$16a^2 - 256 = 9a^2 - 81$$

$$7a^2 = 175$$

$$a^2 = 25$$

$$\underline{a = 5}$$

$$\underline{w = 1}.$$

The maximum speed $= aw$

$$= \underline{5}.$$

The periodic time $= \frac{2\pi}{w} = \underline{2\pi}.$

(a) The amplitude of the SHM = $\underline{5\,\text{m}}$.

(b) The value of $\underline{w = 1}$.

(c) The maximum speed $= \underline{5\,\text{m s}^{-1}}$.

(d) The periodic time $= \underline{2\pi\,\text{s}}$.

EXAMPLE

4

A particle of mass m is fastened to one end A of a light, elastic string AB of natural length a and modulus mg. The other end B of the string is fixed to a point on a smooth plane inclined at $30°$ to the horizontal, so that the string lies down a line of greatest slope.

Find the length of AB when the particle is in equilibrium.

The particle is now pulled down the line of greatest slope from its equilibrium position for a further distance a and then released.

Show that while the string remains taut, the particle will be moving with SHM and find: (a) the speed of the particle when the string slackens; (b) the time taken to reach this position.

SOLUTION

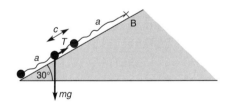

In equilibrium

$$mg \sin 30° = T.$$

Hence $\frac{1}{2}mg = \frac{mg}{a} c$

$$c = \tfrac{1}{2}a.$$

Hooke's law

$$T = \frac{mg}{a} c.$$

Equation of motion up the plane   *Hooke's law*

$$T - mg\sin 30° = -m\ddot{x}.$$ $$T = \frac{mg}{a}\left(\tfrac{1}{2}a + x\right).$$

Hence $\dfrac{mg}{a}\left(\tfrac{1}{2}a + x\right) - \tfrac{1}{2}mg = -m\ddot{x}.$

$$\ddot{x} = -\frac{g}{a}x \qquad \text{i.e. SHM with } w^2 = \frac{g}{a}.$$

To find the speed when the string slackens:

Using $v^2 = w^2(a^2 - x^2)$

$$v^2 = \frac{g}{a}\left(a^2 - \tfrac{1}{4}a^2\right)$$

$$\underline{v = \sqrt{(3ag/4)}.}$$

To find the time taken from C to D:

$$t = \frac{1}{w}\sin^{-1}\left(\frac{x}{a}\right)$$

$$t = \sqrt{\frac{a}{g}}\sin^{-1}\left(\tfrac{1}{2}\right)$$

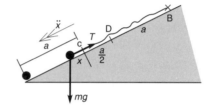

$$= \frac{\pi}{6}\sqrt{\frac{a}{g}} \implies \text{time until string is slack} = \frac{1}{4}\left(\frac{2\pi}{w}\right) + t$$

$$= \sqrt{\frac{a}{g}}\left[\frac{\pi}{2} + \frac{\pi}{6}\right]$$

$$= \frac{2\pi}{3}\sqrt{\frac{a}{g}}.$$

(a) The speed of the particle when the string slackens $= \underline{\sqrt{(3ag/4)}.}$

(b) The time taken from B to D $= \underline{\dfrac{2\pi}{3}\sqrt{\dfrac{a}{g}}.}$

EXAMPLE

5

Two strings AP and BP are attached to a particle P of mass *m*. The string AP is elastic with a natural length of 3*a*, while the string BP is inelastic and 3*a* long. The other ends of the strings A and B are fixed to a horizontal ceiling at a distance 5*a* apart. When the system is hanging in equilibrium, the length AP is 4*a*.

Find: (a) the tensions in the strings when hanging in this position; (b) the modulus of elasticity of the string AP.

If the string BP is now removed and the particle P is allowed to hang in equilibrium from the point A, find the extension now in the string.

If P is now pulled down vertically for a distance *a* and then released: (c) show that the resulting motion is SHM and find its period; (d) find the time taken for P to travel through a distance $\frac{1}{2}a$.

SOLUTION

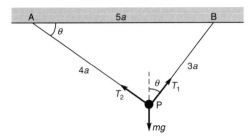

Resolve vertically

$T_1 \cos \theta + T_2 \sin \theta = mg$

$4T_1 + 3T_2 = 5mg.$

Resolve horizontally

$T_1 \sin \theta = T_2 \cos \theta$

$3T_1 = 4T_2.$

Solving $\implies$ $T_1 = \frac{4}{5}mg$ $T_2 = \frac{3}{5}mg.$

Hooke's law

$T_1 = \dfrac{\lambda a}{3a} \implies \frac{3}{5}mg = \dfrac{\lambda}{3} \implies \lambda = \frac{9}{5}mg.$

In equilibrium

$T_0 = mg$

$(9mg/5)(c/3a) = mg \implies c = 5a/3.$

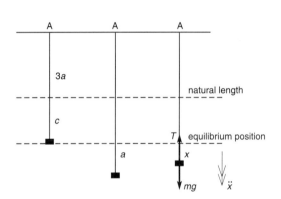

Equation of motion

$T - mg = -m\ddot{x}$

$\frac{9}{5}mg \left(\dfrac{5a/3 + x}{3a} \right) - mg = -m\ddot{x}.$

Hence $\ddot{x} = -\dfrac{3g}{5a}x$, i.e. SHM.

Time period $= 2\pi \sqrt{(5a/3g)}.$

Time from centre of oscillation to a distance $\frac{1}{2}a$ is given by

$t = \dfrac{1}{w} \sin^{-1} \left(\dfrac{x}{a} \right)$ from $x = 0$ to $x = \frac{1}{2}a \implies t = \dfrac{\pi}{6w}.$

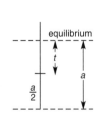

Time taken to travel through a distance $\frac{1}{2}a = \frac{1}{4}T - t$

$= \pi/2w - \pi/6w$

$= \pi/3w.$

(a) The tensions in the strings are $\frac{4}{5}mg$ and $\frac{3}{5}mg.$
(b) The modulus of elasticity is $\frac{9}{5}mg.$
(c) The period of the motion $= 2\pi\sqrt{(5a/3g)}.$
(d) The time taken to travel a distance $\frac{1}{2}a = \dfrac{\pi}{3}\sqrt{(5a/3g)}.$

EXAMPLE

6

A force acts on a particle P of mass 100 g, making it move along the x-axis. It passes through O at time $t = 0$ and its speed (v m s^{-1}) at time t is given by

$$v = 6\cos 3t.$$

Show that the motion of the particle is SHM and find: (a) the amplitude of the motion; (b) the maximum kinetic energy of the particle; (c) the greatest force acting on the particle.

SOLUTION

Differentiating: $\dfrac{dx}{dt} = 6\cos 3t$

Integrating: $\dfrac{d^2x}{dt^2} = -18\sin 3t$

$x = 2\sin 3t + C$

$x = 0$ when $t = 0$ $\Longrightarrow$ $C = 0$

$x = 2\sin 3t.$

Hence it follows that $\dfrac{d^2x}{dt^2} = -9x$,   i.e. SHM with $w^2 = 9$.

$v = 6\cos 3t$ $\Longrightarrow$ Max $v = 6$ (when $t = 0$)

$x = 2\sin 3t$ $\Longrightarrow$ Max $x = 2$ (when $t = \pi/6$) $\Longrightarrow$ amplitude = $\underline{2\,\text{m.}}$

Hence the maximum kinetic energy $= \frac{1}{2}mv^2$

$= \frac{1}{2}(0.1)(6^2)$

$= \underline{1.8\,\text{J.}}$

The maximum acceleration of the particle is given by $aw^2 = 18$.

Hence the maximum force acts on the particles: Max $F = ma$

$= 0.1 \times 18$

$= \underline{1.8.}$

(a) The amplitude of the motion = $\underline{2\,\text{m}}$.

(b) The maximum $KE = \underline{1.8\,\text{J}}$.

(c) The maximum force acting on the particle = $\underline{1.8\,\text{N}}$.

Exercises

1

A particle of mass m is attached to one end of a light, elastic spring of natural length $3a$ and modulus mg. The free end of the spring is now fixed to a point on a smooth table. The particle is now pulled along the table until the spring is $5a$ long and then released.

Show that the subsequent motion is SHM and find: (a) the maximum speed of the particle in the subsequent motion; (b) the maximum force exerted by the spring; (c) the periodic time.

2 A particle of mass m is executing SHM between two points A and B, 60 cm apart.

If it takes 3 s to travel from A to B, find: (a) the amplitude of the motion; (b) the periodic time; (c) the maximum kinetic energy of the particle during the motion.

3 A particle of mass 5 kg executes SHM of period 15 s and amplitude 2 m.

Find: (a) the maximum speed of the particle; (b) the maximum force exerted on the particle; (c) the maximum kinetic energy of the particle; (d) the distance from the centre of the oscillation C to a point P where the particle has half its maximum speed; (e) the time taken to move from C to P.

4 A particle is executing SHM between two points A and B. The point C is the centre of the oscillation. The speed of the particle is $5 \, \text{m s}^{-1}$ when its distance from C is 12 cm. The speed of the particle is $12 \, \text{m s}^{-1}$ when its distance from C is 5 cm.

Find: (a) the amplitude of the motion; (b) the maximum speed of the particle during its motion; (c) the periodic time.

5 A spring of natural length $2a$ and modulus $4mg$ has one end A fixed to a point on a smooth, horizontal table and carries a mass m at its other end B. The spring lies on the table at its natural length when its end B is pulled out, so extending the spring by $3a/2$ and then released.

Show that the subsequent motion is SHM and find the time taken for the particle to move from the extended position to a point C, where $AC = \frac{5}{4}a$.

6 A particle of mass 9 kg is executing SHM of period 24 s and amplitude 4 m, the centre of the oscillation being C.

Find: (a) the maximum kinetic energy of the particle; (b) the speed of the particle when it is at a point P, 2 m from C; (c) the time taken to move from C to P; (d) the distance of the particle from C when its kinetic energy is one quarter of its maximum kinetic energy.

7 A particle of mass m is fastened to one end of a light, elastic string of natural length 6 m and modulus $8.4mg$. The other end of the string is fastened to a point on a smooth plane inclined at 30° to the horizontal, so that the string lies down a line of greatest slope.

The particle is now held so that the length of the string is 7 m and then released. Taking $g = 10 \, \text{m s}^{-2}$ find: (a) the speed of the particle when the string becomes slack; (b) the total distance moved up the plane by the particle.

8 A particle of mass m is fastened to one end B of a light, elastic string AB of natural length a and modulus $2mg$. The other end A is fixed to the ceiling of a room. The particle is now held vertically below A so that $AB = a$, i.e. the string is at its natural length.

If it is then released, find: (a) the equilibrium position of the particle.

Show that the motion is SHM and find: (b) the total depth the particle falls before beginning to rise again; (c) the maximum kinetic energy during the motion.

9 A force acts on a particle P of mass 50 g, making it move along the x-axis. It passes through O at time $t = 0$ and its speed ($v\,\mathrm{m\,s^{-1}}$) at time t is

$v = 8 \cos 4t.$

Show that the motion is SHM and find: (a) the amplitude of the motion; (b) the maximum speed of the particle; (c) the greatest force acting on the particle.

Chapter 13

Variable accelerations

This chapter deals with bodies that are under the action of variable forces, thus producing variable accelerations.

The different forms in which the acceleration can be expressed will be used in this section.

Acceleration:

$$\frac{dv}{dt}.$$

$$v\frac{dv}{dx}.$$

$$\frac{d^2x}{dt^2}.$$

Examples

EXAMPLE

1

A particle is travelling along the x-axis and passes through O when $t = 0$. Its displacement, s metres, from O is given by

$$s = t^3 - 6t^2 + 9t.$$

Find: (a) the time when the particle is next at O; (b) the speed of the particle after 4 s; (c) the times when the particle is instantaneously at rest; (d) the time when the acceleration is zero.

SOLUTION

$$s = t^3 - 6t^2 + 9t$$

$$v = \frac{ds}{dt} = 3t^2 - 12t + 9$$

$$a = \frac{d^2s}{dt} = 6t - 12.$$

Particle is at O when $s = 0 \implies t^3 - 6t^2 + 9t = 0$
$$t(t - 3)^2 = 0.$$

Hence particle is at O when $t = 0$ and $\underline{t = 3}$.

When $t = 4$, $v = 48 - 48 + 9$
$$\underline{v = 9}.$$

Particle has a zero speed when $3t^2 - 12t + 9 = 0$
$$t^2 - 4t + 3 = 0 \implies \underline{t = 1} \quad \text{and} \quad \underline{t = 3}.$$

The acceleration is zero when $6t - 12 = 0 \implies \underline{t = 2}$.

(a) The particle is next at O <u>after 3 s</u>.

(b) The velocity after 4 s = $\underline{9 \, \text{m s}^{-1}}$.

(c) The particle is at rest <u>after 1 s and after 3 s</u>.

(d) The acceleration is zero <u>after 2 s</u>.

EXAMPLE

2

A particle P moves along the x-axis and passes through the origin O at time $t = 0$ with a speed of $36 \, \text{m s}^{-1}$ in the positive x-direction. At time t s after passing O, its acceleration $a \, \text{m s}^{-2}$ is given by

$$a = \frac{dv}{dt} = 6t - 24.$$

Find: (a) the times when the particle comes to instantaneous rest; (b) its distance from O at these times.

Give a brief description of the motion of P.

SOLUTION

To find an expression for v, we have to integrate the acceleration

$$a = \frac{dv}{dt} = 6t - 24$$

$$v = 3t^2 - 24t + A$$

$$\left.\begin{array}{l} v = 36 \\ t = 0 \end{array}\right\} \implies A = 36 \quad v = 3t^2 - 24t + 36.$$

$$\text{When } v = 0: \quad 0 = 3t^2 - 24t + 36$$

$$0 = t^2 - 8t + 12$$

$$0 = (t - 6)(t - 2) \implies \underline{t = 2} \quad \text{and} \quad \underline{t = 6}.$$

To find an expression for s, its displacement from O, we have to integrate the velocity.

$$v = \frac{ds}{dt} = 3t^2 - 24t + 36$$

$$s = t^3 - 12t^2 + 36t + B$$

$$\left.\begin{array}{l} s = 0 \\ t = 0 \end{array}\right\} \implies B = 0 \quad s = t^3 - 12t^2 + 36t.$$

When $t = 2$, $s = 8 - 48 + 72 \implies \underline{s = 32}$.

When $t = 6$, $s = 216 - 432 + 216 \implies \underline{s = 0}$.

(a) The particle is instantaneously at rest when <u>$t = 2$ and $t = 6$ s</u>.

(b) Its distances from O at these times are <u>$s = 32$ and $s = 0$ m</u>.

The particle passes through O with a speed of $36 \, \text{m s}^{-1}$ in the positive x-direction, slows down and comes to instantaneous rest 32 m from O after 2 s. It then returns, coming to rest at O, 6 s later. Finally, it moves again in the positive *x*-direction with increasing acceleration.

EXAMPLE

3

A particle is moving in a straight line when it passes a point A at time $t = 0$. The velocity of the particle is given by

$$v = \frac{ds}{dt} = t^2 - 9t + 18.$$

Find: (a) the speed with which it passes A; (b) the times when it is instantaneously at rest; (c) the distance covered between these two times; (d) the acceleration of the particle at these times.

SOLUTION

$$v = t^2 - 9t + 18.$$

When $t = 0$, $\underline{u = 18}$.

The particle is at rest when $v = 0$.

$$t^2 - 9t + 18 = 0$$

$$(t - 3)(t - 6) = 0 \implies \underline{t = 3} \quad \text{and} \quad \underline{t = 6}.$$

To find an expression for *s*, we have to integrate the velocity.

$$v = \frac{ds}{dt} = t^2 - 9t + 18$$

$$s = \frac{t^3}{3} - \frac{9t^2}{2} + 18t + A$$

$$\left.\begin{array}{l} s = 0 \\ t = 0 \end{array}\right\} \implies A = 0 \quad s = \frac{t^3}{3} - \frac{9t^2}{2} + 18t.$$

When $t = 3$, $s = 22.5$.

When $t = 6$, $s = 18$.

Hence the distance travelled between the two times = $\underline{4.5\,\text{m}}$.

To find the acceleration we have to differentiate *v*.

$$a = \frac{dv}{dt} = 2t - 9.$$

When $t = 3$, $\underline{a = -3}$.

When $t = 6$, $\underline{a = +3}$.

(a) The particle passes through A with a speed of $\underline{18\,\text{m s}^{-1}}$.

(b) The particle is at rest $\underline{\text{after 3 s and after 6 s}}$.

(c) The distance covered between these times = 4.5 m.

(d) The accelerations at the two times are $-3\,\mathrm{m\,s^{-2}}$ and $3\,\mathrm{m\,s^{-2}}$.

EXAMPLE

4

A rocket accelerates in a straight line from rest to a speed of $129.6\,\mathrm{km\,h^{-1}}$ in 1.5 s. The acceleration $a\,\mathrm{m\,s^{-2}}$ of the rocket is given by

$$a = \frac{dv}{dt} = 8t + bt^2 \quad \text{where } b \text{ is a constant.}$$

Show that $129.6\,\mathrm{km\,h^{-1}} = 36\,\mathrm{m\,s^{-1}}$.

Show that $b = 24$ and find the distance covered by the rocket in this time.

SOLUTION

To convert $129.6\,\mathrm{km\,h^{-1}}$ into $\mathrm{m\,s^{-1}}$, we divide by $3.6 \Longrightarrow 36\,\mathrm{m\,s^{-1}}$.

To find an expression for v, we have to integrate the acceleration.

$$a = \frac{dv}{dt} = 8t + bt^2$$

$$v = 4t^2 + b\,\frac{t^3}{3} + A$$

$$\left.\begin{array}{c} v = 0 \\ t = 0 \end{array}\right\} \Longrightarrow A = 0 \quad v = 4t^2 + b\,\frac{t^3}{3}$$

$$\left.\begin{array}{c} v = 36 \\ t = 1.5 \end{array}\right\} \Longrightarrow 36 = 9 + 1.125b$$

$$\underline{b = 24.}$$

To find s, we have to integrate the speed.

$$v = \frac{ds}{dt} = 4t^2 + 8t^3$$

$$s = \frac{4t^3}{3} + 2t^4 + B$$

$$\left.\begin{array}{c} s = 0 \\ t = 0 \end{array}\right\} \Longrightarrow B = 0 \quad s = \frac{4t^3}{3} + 2t^4.$$

When $t = 1.5$, $s = 4.5 + 10.125$

$$\underline{s = 14.625.}$$

The distance covered by the rocket in 1.5 s = $\underline{14.625\,\mathrm{m}}$.

EXAMPLE

5

A particle moves along the positive x axis, starting from rest at O. t seconds later its speed $v\,\mathrm{m\,s^{-1}}$ is given by

$$v = \frac{ds}{dt} = \tfrac{1}{4}(e^{2t} - 1).$$

Answering correct to three significant figures, find: (a) its speed after 2 s; (b) its acceleration after 2 s; (c) the distance it has covered in 2 s.

SOLUTION

When $t = 2$, $v = \frac{1}{4}(e^4 - 1)$
$$\underline{v = 13.4}.$$

To find an expression for a, we have to differentiate the velocity:
$$v = \frac{1}{4}(e^{2t} - 1)$$
$$a = \frac{1}{4} \times 2e^{2t}$$
$$a = \frac{1}{2}e^{2t}.$$

When $t = 2$, $\underline{a = 27.3 \text{ m s}^{-2}}$.

To find an expression for s, its displacement from O, we have to integrate the velocity:
$$v = \frac{1}{4}(e^{2t} - 1)$$
$$s = \frac{1}{8}e^{2t} - \frac{t}{4} + C$$

$$\left.\begin{array}{c} s = 0 \\ t = 0 \end{array}\right\} \implies C = -1/8 \quad s = \frac{1}{8}e^{2t} - \frac{t}{4} - \frac{1}{8}$$

When $t = 2$, $s = \frac{1}{8}e^4 - \frac{1}{2} - \frac{1}{8}$
$$\underline{s = 6.20}.$$

(a) Its speed after 2 s = $\underline{\underline{13.4 \text{ m s}^{-1}}}$.
(b) Its acceleration after 2 s = $\underline{\underline{27.3 \text{ m s}^{-2}}}$.
(c) Its displacement after 2 s = $\underline{\underline{6.20 \text{ m}}}$.

EXAMPLE

6

A particle moves in a straight line and its acceleration $a \text{ m s}^{-2}$ is given by

$$a = 3x^2 + 4x + 17$$

where x is the distance measured in metres from a fixed point A.

If the particle passes through A with a speed of 2 m s^{-1}, find its speed when it is: (a) 3 m from A; (b) 6 m from A.

SOLUTION

$$v\frac{dv}{dx} = 3x^2 + 4x + 17$$

$$\int v\,dv = \int (3x^2 + 4x + 17)\,dx$$

$$\frac{1}{2}v^2 = x^3 + 2x^2 + 17x + C$$

$$\left.\begin{array}{c} v = 2 \\ x = 0 \end{array}\right\} \implies C = 2 \quad v^2 = 2x^3 + 4x^2 + 34x + 4.$$

When $x = 3$, $v^2 = 54 + 36 + 102 + 4$

$$v^2 = 196$$

$$\underline{v = 14}.$$

When $x = 6$, $v^2 = 432 + 144 + 204 + 4$

$$v^2 = 784$$

$$\underline{v = 28}.$$

(a) The speed of the particle when $x = 3$ is $\underline{14\,\text{m}\,\text{s}^{-1}}$.

(b) The speed of the particle when $x = 6$ is $\underline{28\,\text{m}\,\text{s}^{-1}}$.

EXAMPLE

7

A particle is projected vertically from the Earth into space with an initial speed U. It is subject only to Newton's gravitational force, i.e. a force acting on it towards the centre of the Earth of the form km/x^2, where m is the mass of the particle, x is its distance from the centre of the Earth and k is a constant.

Show that the speed of the particle $(v\,\text{m}\,\text{s}^{-1})$ satisfies the equation

$$v^2 = U^2 + \frac{2k}{x} - \frac{2k}{R}, \quad \text{where } R \text{ is the radius of the Earth.}$$

Find: (a) the 'escape velocity' of the particle, i.e. the least value of U for which the particle never turns back towards the Earth; (b) the 'terminal velocity' of the particle, i.e. its final velocity in space.

SOLUTION   *Equation of motion*

$$F = ma$$

$$\frac{km}{x^2} = -mv\frac{dv}{dx}$$

$$\int v\,dv = -\int \frac{k}{x^2}\,dx$$

$$\frac{v^2}{2} = \frac{k}{x} + C$$

$$\left.\begin{array}{l} v = U \\ x = R \end{array}\right\} \implies \frac{U^2}{2} = \frac{k}{R} + C \implies C = \frac{U^2}{2} - \frac{k}{R}.$$

Hence $\dfrac{v^2}{2} = \dfrac{U^2}{2} + \dfrac{k}{x} - \dfrac{k}{R}$

$$\underline{v^2 = U^2 + \frac{2k}{x} - \frac{2k}{R}}.$$

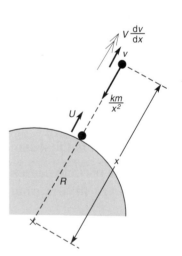

The escape velocity is such that v is always positive for all x, i.e. $U^2 > \dfrac{2k}{R}$.

The terminal velocity is the value of v as x tends to infinity $v^2 \to U^2 - \dfrac{2k}{R}$.

(a) For the particle to escape from the Earth $\underline{U > \sqrt{(2k/R)}}$.

(b) The speed of the particle will tend to a value $\underline{\sqrt{(U^2 - 2k/R)}}$.

EXAMPLE

8

A van of mass 2 tonnes has an engine that can produce a maximum power of 48 kW. The total resistance to its motion is of the form $(p + qv)$, where v is the speed of the van in $\mathrm{m\,s^{-1}}$ and p and q are constants. The van maintains a maximum steady speed of $180\,\mathrm{km\,h^{-1}}$ on the level. It can ascend a hill with a maximum steady speed of $108\,\mathrm{km\,h^{-1}}$ where the inclination of the hill is $\sin^{-1}(0.04)$ to the horizontal.

By modelling the van as a particle, show that $p = 600$ and $q = 7.2$.

The van now travels on the level at $126\,\mathrm{km\,h^{-1}}$ when the engine is shut off.

Find, correct to three significant figures, the time from when the engine is shut off to when it comes to rest.

SOLUTION

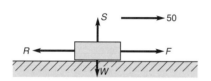
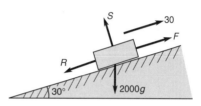

We use the conversion factor 3.6 to change the speeds in $\mathrm{km\,h^{-1}}$ to $\mathrm{m\,s^{-1}}$.

$$180\,\mathrm{km\,h^{-1}} = 50\,\mathrm{m\,s^{-1}} \qquad 108\,\mathrm{km\,h^{-1}} = 30\,\mathrm{m\,s^{-1}} \qquad 126\,\mathrm{km\,h^{-1}} = 35\,\mathrm{m\,s^{-1}}.$$

The tractive force $F = \dfrac{\text{power}}{\text{velocity}}$.

Van on the level   *Van moving up the hill*

$$F = R \qquad\qquad\qquad\qquad\qquad\qquad F = R + mg\sin\theta$$

$$\frac{48\,000}{50} = p + 50q \qquad\qquad\qquad \frac{48\,000}{30} = p + 30q + (2000)(9.8)(0.04)$$

$$\underline{960 = p + 50q}. \qquad\qquad\qquad\qquad 1600 = p + 30q + 784$$

$$\qquad\qquad\qquad\qquad\qquad\qquad\qquad\qquad \underline{816 = p + 30q}.$$

Solving these two equations we get: $\underline{\underline{p = 600}}$ $\underline{\underline{q = 7.2}}$.

Equation of motion on the level

$$R = -ma$$

$$p + qv = -m\,\frac{dv}{dt}$$

$$\int dt = -m \int \frac{dv}{p + qv}$$

$$t = \frac{-m}{q} \ln\left[p + qv\right]_{35}^{0}$$

$$t = \frac{m}{q} \ln\left[\frac{p + 35q}{p}\right]$$

$$= \underline{97.4}.$$

The time taken for the van to come to rest $= \underline{\underline{97.4\,\mathrm{s}}}$.

EXAMPLE

9

A particle of mass m falls vertically from rest under gravity and through a medium which produces a resistance to its motion of mkv^2 newtons, where m is the mass of the particle, v its speed in $\mathrm{m\,s^{-1}}$, and k is a constant.

If the vertical distance through the medium is a, show that the speed of the particle as it exits from the medium is given by

$$v^2 = \frac{g}{k}\left(1 - \mathrm{e}^{-2ka}\right).$$

SOLUTION   *Equation of motion*

$$\text{Force} = \text{mass} \times \text{acceleration}$$

$$mg - mkv^2 = mv\frac{dv}{dx}$$

$$\int x\,dx = \int \frac{v}{(g - kv^2)}\,dv$$

$$x = -\frac{1}{2k}\ln(g - kv^2) + C$$

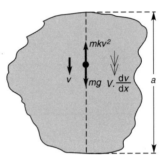

$$\left.\begin{array}{l} x = 0 \\ v = 0 \end{array}\right\} \implies C = \frac{1}{2k}\ln(g)$$

$$x = -\frac{1}{2k}\ln(g - kv^2) + \frac{1}{2k}\ln(g)$$

$$x = -\frac{1}{2k}\ln\left(\frac{g - kv^2}{g}\right).$$

Taking exponentials

$$g\,\mathrm{e}^{-2kx} = g - kv^2.$$

When $x = a$, $v^2 = \dfrac{g}{k}\left(1 - \mathrm{e}^{-2ka}\right).$

The speed with which the particle exits from the medium is given by

$$v^2 = \frac{g}{k}\left(1 - \mathrm{e}^{-2ka}\right).$$

EXAMPLE

10

A car of mass $300\,\mathrm{kg}$ is travelling along a straight, level road with speed $v\,\mathrm{m\,s^{-1}}$. The resistance to its motion is constant of magnitude $1200\,\mathrm{N}$. The engine of the car produces a constant power $48\,\mathrm{kW}$.

Show that

$$40 - v = \tfrac{1}{4}v\frac{dv}{dt}.$$

Find the time taken for the car to increase its speed from $72\,\mathrm{km\,h^{-1}}$ to $108\,\mathrm{km\,h^{-1}}$.

SOLUTION

Equation of motion

$$F - R = ma$$

$$\frac{48\,000}{v} - 1200 = 300\,\frac{dv}{dt}$$

$$\frac{160}{v} - 4 = \frac{dv}{dt}$$

$$40 - v = \tfrac{1}{4}v\,\frac{dv}{dt}.$$

Separating the variables:

$$4\int dt = \int \frac{v}{40 - v}\,dv$$

$$4t = -\int\left(1 - \frac{40}{40 - v}\right) dv$$

$$4t = \left[-v - 40\ln(40 - v)\right]_{20}^{30}$$

$$4t = \left[-30 - 40\ln(10)\right] - \left[-20 - 40\ln(20)\right]$$

$$4t = 40\ln 2 - 10$$

$$t = 10\ln 2 - 2\tfrac{1}{2}$$

$$\underline{t = 4.43}.$$

The car increases its speed from $72\,\text{km h}^{-1}$ to $108\,\text{km h}^{-1}$ in $\underline{4.43\,\text{s}}$.

Exercises

1 A particle is travelling along the x axis and passes through O at time $t = 0$. Its displacement $x\,\text{m}$ from O is given by

$$x = 2t^3 - 33t^2 + 168t.$$

Find: (a) the times when the particle is instantaneously at rest; (b) its displacement from O at these times; (c) its acceleration at these times.

2 A particle moves along the x axis and passes through the origin with a speed of $63\,\text{m s}^{-1}$ at time $t = 0$. The acceleration $a\,\text{m s}^{-2}$ of the particle t seconds after passing O is

$$a = 6(t - 5).$$

Find: (a) the times when the particle is instantaneously at rest; (b) the distance travelled between these two times.

3 A car is travelling along a straight, level road from rest at $t = 0$ and its acceleration $a\,\mathrm{m\,s^{-2}}$ is given by

$a = 6 + kt$ where k is a constant.

From rest, the car gains a speed of $45\,\mathrm{m\,s^{-1}}$ in $10\,\mathrm{s}$.

Show that $k = -0.3$, and find the distance covered in this time.

4 A particle is moving in a straight line from a point A at time $t = 0$, such that its speed $v\,\mathrm{m\,s^{-1}}$ is given by

$10v = e^{2t} - 12t$.

Answering correct to three significant figures, find: (a) its speed after $2\,\mathrm{s}$; (b) its displacement from A after $2\,\mathrm{s}$; (c) the time when its acceleration is zero.

5 A particle P moves in a straight line and its acceleration $a\,\mathrm{m\,s^{-2}}$ is given by

$a = x^2 - 2x + 12$

where x is its displacement in metres from a fixed point A. The particle passes through A at time $t = 0$ with a speed of $2\,\mathrm{m\,s^{-1}}$.

Find: (a) the speed of P when it is $12\,\mathrm{m}$ from A; (b) the speed of P when it is $57\,\mathrm{m}$ from A.

6 A train of mass 150 tonnes has an engine that can exert a maximum power of $300\,\mathrm{kW}$. The total resistance to its motion can be expressed in the form $p + qv$, where p and q are constants, and v is the speed of the train in $\mathrm{m\,s^{-1}}$. The maximum speed of the train on the level is $180\,\mathrm{km\,h^{-1}}$. The maximum speed of the train when ascending a hill of inclination $\sin^{-1}(0.003)$ to the horizontal is $108\,\mathrm{km\,h^{-1}}$.

Show that $p = 4975$ and $q = 20.5$.

The train now travels again on the level, but at $171\,\mathrm{km\,h^{-1}}$ when the engine is shut off. Find the time that elapses after the engine is shut off before it is brought to rest.

7 A particle of mass m falls from rest under gravity and through a medium that offers a resistance to its motion of mkv newtons, where m is its mass, v its speed in $\mathrm{m\,s^{-1}}$, and k is a constant.

Show that at time t after entering the medium, its speed is given by

$$v = \frac{g}{k}\left(1 - e^{-kt}\right).$$

8 A car of mass $600\,\mathrm{kg}$ is travelling in a straight line on the level with speed of $v\,\mathrm{m\,s^{-1}}$. The resistance to its motion is constant and of magnitude $900\,\mathrm{N}$. If the engine of the car is exerting its maximum power of $36\,\mathrm{kW}$, show that

$$3(40 - v) = 2v\,\frac{dv}{dt}.$$

Find the time taken for the car to increase its speed from $54\,\mathrm{km\,h^{-1}}$ to $108\,\mathrm{km\,h^{-1}}$ under this maximum power.

9 A particle of mass m falls from rest under gravity through a medium that produces a resistance to its motion of magnitude kmv^2, where m is the mass of the particle, v is its speed in $\mathrm{m\,s}^{-1}$ and k is a constant.

What is the terminal speed of the particle in terms of g and k?

Find, correct to two decimal places, the distance fallen by the particle when it acquired half its terminal speed, given that $k = 0.005$.

Chapter 14

Vector mechanics

This chapter deals with motion in two or three dimensions, using vector notations for displacement, velocity and acceleration.

The vector r is the displacement vector.

The vector v is the velocity vector.

The vector a is the acceleration vector.

Displacement:	r.
Velocity:	$v = \dfrac{\mathrm{d}r}{\mathrm{d}t}$.
Acceleration:	$a = \dfrac{\mathrm{d}v}{\mathrm{d}t}$.

Examples

EXAMPLE 1

The position vector of a particle P is

$$r = (\cos 3t)i - (\sin 3t)j \text{ metres}$$

relative to a fixed point O, where t is the time measured in seconds.

Find: (a) the velocity vector at time t; (b) the speed of P.

SOLUTION

$$r = (\cos 3t)i - (\sin 3t)j$$

$$v = \frac{\mathrm{d}r}{\mathrm{d}t} = (-3 \sin 3t)i - (3 \cos 3t)j.$$

The speed of the particle is the magnitude of the velocity.

$$v = |v|$$

$$v = \sqrt{[(-3 \sin 3t)^2 + (-3 \cos 3t)^2]}$$

$$v = \sqrt{[9(\sin^2 3t + \cos^2 3t)]}$$

$$\underline{v = 3}.$$

(a) The velocity vector $= \begin{bmatrix} -3 \sin 3t \\ -3 \cos 3t \end{bmatrix}$.

(b) The speed of the particle has a constant value $\underline{\underline{3 \text{ m s}^{-1}}}$.

EXAMPLE

2

The position vector r m of a particle at time t s, relative to a fixed point O, is

$r = t^2 i + 3t j$.

Find the speed of the particle after 2 s.

SOLUTION

$r = t^2 i + 3t j$

$v = \dfrac{dr}{dt} = 2t i + 3j$.

When $t = 2$, $v = 4i + 3j$.

The speed of the particle is the magnitude of the velocity vector

$|v| = \sqrt{(4^2 + 3^2)}$

$= \underline{5}$.

After 2 s the speed of the particle is $\underline{\underline{5\,m\,s^{-1}}}$.

EXAMPLE

3

A particle moves in the horizontal plane and its velocity vector $v\,m\,s^{-1}$ is given by

$v = (-2 \sin t)i + t^2 j$

where t is the time in seconds.

Find the acceleration vector a.

If initially the position vector of the particle is $3i + 2j$, find the displacement vector at time t seconds.

SOLUTION

$v = (-2 \sin t)i + t^2 j$.

To find the acceleration we have to differentiate v

$\underline{a = (-2 \cos t)i + 2t j}$.

To find the displacement we have to integrate v

$r = (2 \cos t + A)i + \left(\dfrac{t^3}{3} + B\right)j$.

When $t = 0$, $r = 3i + 2j$ $\implies$ $A = 1$ $B = 2$

Hence

$\underline{\underline{r = (2 \cos t + 1)i + \left(\dfrac{t^3}{3} + 2\right)j}}$.

EXAMPLE

4

A ball of mass 40 g is travelling with velocity $v\,m\,s^{-1}$, where

$v = 3i + j$.

The ball is given an impulse which results in an instantaneous change in velocity to $7i + j$.

Find: (a) the magnitude of the impulse; (b) the angle the impulse vector makes with i, answering to the nearest degree.

SOLUTION   Impulse J = change in momentum:

$$J = m(v_2 - v_1)$$

$$= 0.04[(7i + 4j) - (3i + j)]$$

$$= 0.04(4i + 3j).$$

The magnitude of the impulse is

$$|J| = 0.04 \times \sqrt{(4^2 + 3^2)}$$

$$|J| = 0.2\,\text{N s.}$$

The angle J makes with i can be seen from the diagram:

$$\tan \theta = 0.75$$

$$\underline{\theta = 37°} \quad \text{(nearest degree).}$$

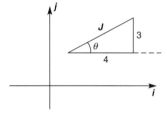

(a) The magnitude of the impulse = <u>0.2 N s</u>.

(b) The angle the direction of the impulse makes with i = <u>37°</u>.

EXAMPLE

5   **A particle moves in the horizontal plane and its displacement vector r metres from a fixed point O at time t seconds is**

$$r = (t^2 - 4t)i + \left(5t - \tfrac{1}{2}t^2\right)j.$$

Find the velocity vector v and hence find the times when the particle is moving:
(a) parallel to i; (b) parallel to j; (c) parallel to $i + j$.

SOLUTION $r = (t^2 - 4t)i + \left(5t - \tfrac{1}{2}t^2\right)j.$

To find the velocity we have to differentiate r

$$v = (2t - 4)i + (5 - t)j.$$

If v is parallel to i, the j component must be zero.

Hence $5 - t = 0$

$$\underline{t = 5}.$$

If v is parallel to j, the i component must be zero.

Hence $2t - 4 = 0$

$$\underline{t = 2}.$$

If v is parallel to $i + j$, the i component equals the j component.

Hence $2t - 4 = 5 - t$

$$\underline{t = 3}.$$

(a) The particle is travelling parallel to i after <u>5 s</u>.

(b) The particle is travelling parallel to j after <u>2 s</u>.

(c) The particle is travelling parallel to $i + j$ after <u>3 s</u>.

EXAMPLE

6

A particle is moving in the $x-y$ plane under the action of a force F where

$F = 5i + 12j$.

Find the magnitude of this force.

The force F is the resultant of two forces P and Q.

The line of action of P is parallel to $i + 8j$.

The line of action of Q is parallel to $i + j$.

Determine the vectors P and Q.

SOLUTION

$F = 5i + 12j$

$|F| = \sqrt{(5^2 + 12^2)}$

$\underline{|F| = 13.}$

The force F is the sum of the vectors P and Q.

$$F = P + Q$$

$$\begin{bmatrix} 5 \\ 12 \end{bmatrix} = s\begin{bmatrix} 1 \\ 8 \end{bmatrix} + t\begin{bmatrix} 1 \\ 1 \end{bmatrix} \quad \text{where } s \text{ and } t \text{ are constants.}$$

It follows that

$$\left.\begin{array}{l} s + t = 5 \\ 8s + t = 12 \end{array}\right\}.$$

Solving these we get: $s = 1$ and $t = 4$.

Hence $P = \begin{bmatrix} 1 \\ 8 \end{bmatrix} \quad Q = \begin{bmatrix} 4 \\ 4 \end{bmatrix}$.

EXAMPLE

7

A particle is moving in space so that its displacement vector r metres relative to a fixed point O after t s is given by

$$r = \begin{bmatrix} t - 2 \\ 2t^2 \\ 2 - 4t \end{bmatrix}.$$

Find: (a) the distance of the particle from O after 2 s; (b) the speed of the particle after 2 s.

SOLUTION

Differentiating the displacement vector we get

$$v = \begin{bmatrix} 1 \\ 4t \\ -4 \end{bmatrix}.$$

When $t = 2$, the magnitude of $r = |r| = \sqrt{(0 + 8^2 + 6^2)}$

$$= \underline{10}.$$

When $t = 2$, the magnitude of the velocity $v = |\boldsymbol{v}| = \sqrt{(1^2 + 8^2 + 4^2)}$

$$= \underline{9}.$$

(a) After 2 s the particle is $\underline{10\,\text{m}}$ from O.

(b) After 2 s the speed of the particle is $\underline{9\,\text{m}\,\text{s}^{-1}}$.

EXAMPLE

8

A particle is moving in the $x-y$ plane and its displacement vector r metres, relative to the origin, is

$$r = \begin{bmatrix} 2t^3 \\ bt^2 + 4t \end{bmatrix}$$

where b is a constant, and t is the time measured in seconds.

Given that when $t = 2$ the velocity vector v is parallel to $i + j$, find the value of b.

Find also the magnitude of the acceleration when $t = 2$.

SOLUTION

Differentiating the displacement vector we get

$$v = \begin{bmatrix} 6t^2 \\ 2bt + 4 \end{bmatrix}.$$

Differentiating the velocity vector we get

$$a = \begin{bmatrix} 12t \\ 2b \end{bmatrix}.$$

Since $\boldsymbol{v}$ is parallel to $\boldsymbol{i} + \boldsymbol{j}$ when $t = 2$, it follows that the components are equal.

$$24 = 4b + 4$$

$$\underline{b = 5}.$$

When $t = 2$, $\quad a = 24\boldsymbol{i} + 10\boldsymbol{j}$.

Hence $\quad |a| = \sqrt{(24^2 + 10^2)}$

$$= \underline{26}.$$

(a) The value of $\underline{b = 5}$.

(b) The magnitude of the acceleration when $t = 2$ is $\underline{26\,\text{m}\,\text{s}^{-2}}$.

EXAMPLE

9

Two particles A and B are simultaneously moving in the $x-y$ plane. At time $t = 0$, A is passing through the point P$(-1, -1)$ with a velocity

$$v_\text{A} = 3\boldsymbol{i} + 5\boldsymbol{j}$$

while particle B is passing through Q$(7, 3)$ with a velocity

$$v_\text{B} = \boldsymbol{i} + 4\boldsymbol{j}.$$

Show that A and B collide and find the point of their collision.

Also find the time when the particles are $6\sqrt{5}\,\text{m}$ apart.

SOLUTION   We set up the vector equations of the lines of motion of A and B.

These are of the form $r = a + tv$, where a is the point through which the line passes, v is the velocity of the particle, and t is the time that has elapsed in seconds.

Vector line for A   *Vector line for B*

$$r = \begin{bmatrix} -1 \\ -1 \end{bmatrix} + t \begin{bmatrix} 3 \\ 5 \end{bmatrix}.$$ $$r = \begin{bmatrix} 7 \\ 3 \end{bmatrix} + t \begin{bmatrix} 1 \\ 4 \end{bmatrix}.$$

If the lines intersect we require

$$-1 + 3t = 7 + t \qquad \qquad \text{(i)}$$

$$-1 + 5t = 3 + 4t \qquad \qquad \text{(ii)}$$

Equation (i) produces $t = 4$. Only if this satisfies (ii) will the lines intersect. Equation (ii) also produces $t = 4$.

Hence the lines of motion of A and B do intersect at $r = 11i + 19j$.

Let d be the distance between the two particles at time t.

$$d^2 = (8 - 2t)^2 + (4 - t)^2.$$

Hence $(8 - 2t)^2 + (4 - t)^2 = (6\sqrt{5})^2.$

$$5t^2 - 40t - 100 = 0$$

$$t^2 - 8t - 20 = 0$$

$$(t - 10)(t + 2) = 0$$

$$t = 10.$$

The particles are $6\sqrt{5}$ m apart after $\underline{10\,\text{s}}$.

Exercises

1 A particle is travelling in the x–y plane so that its displacement vector r metres, relative to the origin, is

$$r = 2t^3 i - 9t^2 j$$

where t is the time in seconds.

Find: (a) the speed of the particle after 4 s; (b) the acceleration of the particle after 2 s.

2 A particle moves in the x–y plane so that its displacement vector r metres, relative to the origin, is

$$r = t^3 i + (7t^2 - 192t) j$$

where t is the time in seconds.

Find its velocity and acceleration vectors.

Show that after 8 s: (a) the speed of the particle is $208\,\text{m s}^{-1}$; (b) the magnitude of its acceleration is $50\,\text{m s}^{-2}$.

3 A particle is moving in the horizontal plane and its displacement vector r metres, relative to a fixed point O, at time t s is

$$r = (2t^3 - 15t^2)i + (3t^2 - 48t)j.$$

Find the times when the particle is moving: (a) parallel to i; (b) parallel to j; (c) parallel to $i + j$.

4 A ball of mass 100 g is moving in the x–y plane with velocity $(-4i + 4j)\,\mathrm{m\,s^{-1}}$. What angle does its direction of motion make with j?

The ball is now given an impulse $K\,\mathrm{N\,s}$, which instantaneously changes its velocity to $(4i - 2j)\,\mathrm{m\,s^{-1}}$.

Find the magnitude of the impulse K.

5 A ball of mass 500 g is moving in the x–y plane with velocity $(4i + 4j)\,\mathrm{m\,s^{-1}}$ when it is given an impulse $K = 0.5i\,\mathrm{N\,s}$.

Find: (a) the new velocity of the particle; (b) the angle through which the direction of motion of the particle is deflected, answering correct to three significant figures.

6 A particle is moving in the horizontal plane under the action of a force F newtons.

$$F = 8i + 15j.$$

Find the magnitude of this force.

The force F is the resultant of two other forces P and Q. If P is parallel to i and Q is parallel to $2i + 5j$, find the vectors P and Q.

7 A particle is moving in space and its displacement vector, in metres, relative to a fixed point O at time t seconds, is given by

$$r = t^2 i + (t + 5)j + (8t - 12)k.$$

Find: (a) the distance of the particle from O after 2 s; (b) the speed of the particle after 2 s.

8 A particle A is moving in space and passes through the point $P(2, 1, 3)$ with velocity $(i + j + 4k)\,\mathrm{m\,s^{-1}}$, and at the same time another particle B is passing through the point $Q(1, 1, 7)$ with velocity $(2i + j)\,\mathrm{m\,s^{-1}}$.

Show that the two particles collide and find the point of collision.

9 A particle of unit mass is acted upon by two forces P and Q, where P has a constant magnitude of 9 N in the direction $i - 8j + 4k$. Q has a variable magnitude of $4t$ N, where t is the time in seconds, in the direction i.

Find the acceleration vector of the particle.

If when $t = 0$ the velocity of the particle is $-8i + 10j - 5k$, find its speed after 2 s.

10 A ball of mass 0.4 kg is moving with velocity $(5\boldsymbol{i} + 12\boldsymbol{j})\,\mathrm{m\,s^{-1}}$ when it is acted on by an impulse $\boldsymbol{P}$, which instantaneously changes its velocity to $(-13\boldsymbol{i} - 12\boldsymbol{j})\,\mathrm{m\,s^{-1}}$.

Find: (a) the initial speed of the ball; (b) the magnitude of $\boldsymbol{P}$ in N s.

Subsequently the ball is acted on by another impulse $\boldsymbol{Q} = 3.2\boldsymbol{i}$ N s. Show that the ball is finally moving with the same speed as originally but in the opposite direction.

Chapter 15

Centres of gravity

This chapter deals with questions involving the centres of gravity of plane and solid figures, including composite bodies.

Triangular lamina:	intersection of its medians.
Solid hemisphere radius a:	$\dfrac{3a}{8}$ from the centre of the base.
Hollow hemisphere radius a:	$\dfrac{a}{2}$ from the centre of the base.
Solid cone of height h:	$\dfrac{h}{4}$ from the centre of the base.
Hollow cone of height h:	$\dfrac{h}{3}$ from the centre of the base.
Semicircular arc of radius a:	$\dfrac{2a}{\pi}$ from the mid-point of diameter.
Semicircular lamina radius a:	$\dfrac{4a}{3\pi}$ from the mid-point of diameter.

Examples

EXAMPLE

1

A uniform piece of wire of length $7a$ is bent so as to form a letter 'L' as shown. $AB = 4a$, $BC = 3a$ and angle $ABC = 90°$.

(a) Find the distance of the centre of gravity of the figure from: AB and BC.

If the wire is now freely suspended from point A and hangs in equilibrium, (b) find, to the nearest degree, the angle that AB makes with the vertical.

SOLUTION

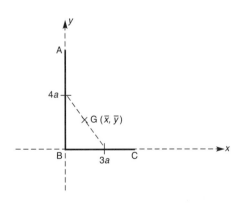

Let the mass per unit length be ρ.

Moments about By

$$3a\rho \times \frac{3a}{2} = 7a\rho \times \bar{x}$$

$$\bar{x} = \frac{9a}{14}.$$

Moments about Bx

$$4a\rho \times 2a = 7a\rho \times \bar{y}$$

$$\bar{y} = \frac{8a}{7}.$$

If the figure is now freely suspended from the point A, then G must be vertically below A.

$$\tan\theta = \frac{PG}{AP}$$

$$= \frac{9a}{14} \div \frac{20a}{7}$$

$$= \frac{9}{40}$$

$$\theta = 13°.$$

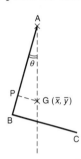

(a) The centre of gravity is at a distance $\dfrac{9a}{14}$ from AB and $\dfrac{8a}{7}$ from BC.

(b) The angle that AB makes with the vertical $= \underline{\underline{13°}}$.

EXAMPLE

2

A uniform piece of wire 30 cm long is bent to form a right-angled triangle with sides 5 cm, 12 cm and 13 cm.

Find the distance of the centre of gravity from: (a) the shorter side; (b) the middle side.

SOLUTION Let the mass per cm be ρ.

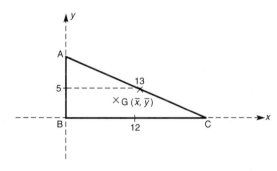

Moments about By

$$(13\rho \times 6) + (12\rho \times 6) = 30\rho \times \bar{x}$$

$$\bar{x} = 5.$$

Moments about Bx

$$\left(13\rho \times \tfrac{5}{2}\right) + \left(5\rho \times \tfrac{5}{2}\right) = 30\rho \times \bar{y}$$

$$\bar{y} = 1.5.$$

The centre of gravity is $\underline{5\,\text{cm}}$ from the shorter side and $\underline{1.5\,\text{cm}}$ from the middle side.

EXAMPLE

3

A uniform, plane rectangle ABCD has AB = 4a and BC = 6a. A square of side 2a is now cut out from the rectangle, one of its vertices coinciding with B.

Find the distance of the centre of gravity of the remaining plane figure from (a) AB; (b) BC.

SOLUTION   Let the mass per unit area be ρ.

Mass of square $= 4a^2\rho = M$.

Mass of rectangle $= 24a^2\rho = 6M$.

Mass of remainder $= 5M$.

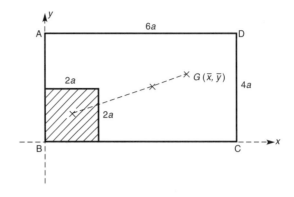

Moments about By

$(6M \times 3a) - (M \times a) = 5M \times \bar{x}$

$17a = 5\bar{x}$

$\bar{x} = \dfrac{17a}{5}$.

Moments about Bx

$(6M \times 2a) - (M \times a) = 5M \times \bar{y}$

$11a = 5y$

$\bar{y} = \dfrac{11a}{5}$.

The centre of gravity is at a distance $\dfrac{17a}{5}$ from AB and $\dfrac{11a}{5}$ from BC.

EXAMPLE

4

A uniform, plane figure is in the form of an isosceles triangle with sides 5 cm, 5 cm and 8 cm. A small isosceles triangle of sides 2.5 cm, 2.5 cm and 4 cm is now cut out as shown.

Find the distance of the centre of gravity of the remaining plane figure from the 8 cm side.

SOLUTION   Let the mass per cm^2 be ρ.

Using Pythagoras, the height of the large triangle $= 3$ cm and that of the small triangle $= 1.5$ cm.

Mass of small triangle $= 3\rho = M$.
Mass of large triangle $= 12\rho = 4M$.
Mass of remaining figure $= 3M$.

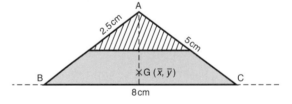

Moments about BC

$(4M \times 1) - (M \times 2) = 3M \times \bar{x}$

$\bar{x} = \tfrac{2}{3}$.

The centre of gravity lies $\tfrac{2}{3}$ cm from BC.

EXAMPLE

5

A uniform, plane figure is in the shape of a circle, centre C and radius $5a$. A smaller circle of radius $2a$ has centre D and its circumference passes through C.

Find the distance of the centre of gravity of the remainder from C.

SOLUTION Let the mass per unit area be ρ.

Mass of small circular lamina $= 4\pi a^2 \rho = 4M$.
Mass of large circular lamina $= 25\pi a^2 \rho = 25M$.
Mass of the remaining lamina $= 21M$.

Moments about Cy

$4M \times 2 = 21M \times \bar{x}$

$\bar{x} = 8a/21$.

The distance of the centre of gravity from C $= 8a/21$.

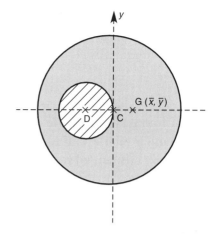

EXAMPLE

6

A uniform, plane, semicircular lamina has radius $3a$ and centre C. A smaller, semicircular section of radius $2a$ is now cut out of the original, its centre coinciding with C.

Find the centre of gravity of the remaining figure.

If this figure is now hung on a rough peg P such that the common diameters are vertical, find the angle that CP makes with the vertical.

SOLUTION Let the mass per unit area be ρ.

Mass of small semicircle $= 2\pi a^2 \rho = 4M$.
Mass of large semicircle $= 4.5\pi a^2 \rho = 9M$.
Mass of remaining figure $= 5M$.

Moments about Cy

$$\left(9M \times \frac{4(3a)}{3\pi}\right) - \left(4M \times \frac{4(2a)}{3\pi}\right) = 5M \times \bar{x}$$

$$\frac{76a}{3\pi} = 5\bar{x}$$

$$\bar{x} = \frac{76a}{15\pi}.$$

If the remaining lamina is to rest as shown:

$$\sin a = \frac{CG}{CP}$$

$$\sin a = \frac{76a}{15\pi} \times \frac{1}{2a}$$

$$a = 54°.$$

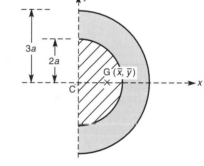

(a) The centre of gravity is at a distance $76a/15\pi$ from C.

(b) The angle that CP makes with the vertical is $54°$.

EXAMPLE

7

A framework is made of uniform wire and takes the form of a letter 'D', i.e. a semicircular arc of radius a, centre C, and diameter PQ. The wire framework is now freely suspended from P so that it hangs in equilibrium.

Find, to the nearest degree, the angle that PQ makes with the vertical.

SOLUTION

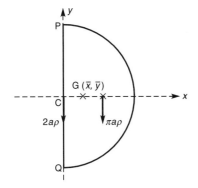

Firstly we will have to find the centre of gravity G of the composite body.

This point G will be vertically below P when the wire hangs in equilibrium.

Let the mass per unit length be ρ.

Mass of semicircular arc $= \pi a \rho$.

Mass of diameter $= 2a\rho$.

Mass of whole figure $= (\pi + 2)a\rho$.

Moments about Cy

$$\pi a \rho \times \frac{2a}{\pi} = (\pi + 2)a\rho \times \bar{x}$$

$$\bar{x} = \frac{2a}{2 + \pi}.$$

If the wire is now suspended from A, we require point G to be vertically below A as shown:

$$\tan \theta = \frac{CG}{CP}$$

$$= \frac{2a}{2 + \pi} \times \frac{1}{a}$$

$$= \frac{2}{2 + \pi}$$

Hence $\theta = 21°$.

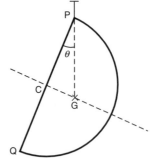

The diameter makes an angle of $21°$ with the vertical when the wire is hanging in equilibrium.

EXAMPLE

8

A composite body is made up of a cone of height a and base radius a, a cylinder of height $3a$ and base radius a, and a hemisphere of radius a. They are all uniform and solid and made of the same material. They are fastened together by their common bases as shown.

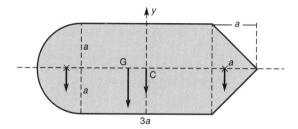

Find the distance of the centre of gravity G from the centre of the cylinder C.

SOLUTION

Let the mass per unit volume be ρ.

Mass of hemisphere $= \frac{2}{3}\pi a^3 \rho = 2M.$

Mass of cylinder $= \pi a^2 (3a)\rho = 9M.$

Mass of cone $= \frac{1}{3}\pi a^2 (a)\rho = M.$

Hence the total mass of the composite $= 12M$.

Moments about Cy

$$2M\left(\frac{3a}{8} + \frac{3a}{2}\right) - M\left(\frac{3a}{2} + \frac{a}{4}\right) = 12M \times \bar{x}$$

$$\frac{15a}{4} - \frac{7a}{4} = 12\bar{x}$$

$$2a = 12\bar{x}$$

$$\underline{\bar{x} = \frac{a}{6}.}$$

The centre of gravity is at a distance $\underline{\underline{\dfrac{a}{6}}}$ from the centre of the cylinder.

EXAMPLE

9

A composite body is made up of a solid hemisphere of radius a and a solid cylinder of height $16a$ and base radius a, joined together by their common base. They are both uniform and made of the same material.

Find the distance of the centre of gravity G of the composite body from the common base.

The body is now placed on an inclined plane which is rough enough to prevent sliding with the free base of the cylinder in contact with the plane.

Find, to the nearest 0.1°, the inclination of the plane to the horizontal if the body is in limiting equilibrium.

SOLUTION

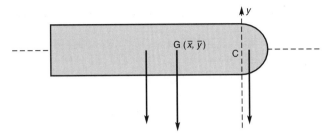

Let the mass per unit volume be ρ.

Mass of hemisphere $= \quad \frac{2}{3}\pi a^3 \rho = M$.

Mass of cylinder $\quad = \pi a^2 (16a)\rho = 24M$.

Hence the mass of the composite $= 25M$.

Moments about Cy

$$(24M \times 8a) - \left(M \times \tfrac{3}{8}a\right) = 25M \times \bar{x}$$

$$1533a = 200\bar{x}$$

$$\bar{x} = 7.665a.$$

Equilibrium can only be destroyed by tilting over of the body. This limiting position will occur when G lies vertically above A.

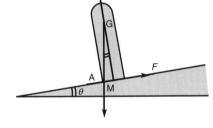

From the diagram

$$\tan\theta = \frac{AM}{GM}$$

$$= \frac{a}{8.335a}$$

$$\theta = 6.8°.$$

The centre of gravity is at a distance of <u>7.665a</u> from the common base.

The largest inclination of the plane $= \underline{\underline{6.8°}}$.

Exercises

1

A uniform piece of wire of length $6a$ is bent so as to form three sides of a square ABCD.

Find the position of the centre of gravity from the middle side BC.

If the wire is now freely suspended from its free end A and hangs in equilibrium, find, to the nearest degree, the angle that AB makes with the vertical.

2

A uniform piece of wire 56 cm long is bent to form the sides of a right-angled triangle with sides 7 cm, 24 cm and 25 cm.

Find the distance of the centre of gravity of the figure from: (a) the shortest side; (b) the middle side.

3 A uniform, plane square with sides of 4 cm has a rectangular piece cut from it as shown.

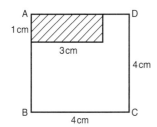

Find the centre of gravity of the resulting lamina from (a) BC; (b) DC.

If this lamina is now freely suspended from the vertex D, find the angle that DC makes with the vertical, answering to the nearest degree.

4 A uniform, plane lamina is in the form of a right-angled triangle ABC. A small right-angled triangle AXY is now cut from it as shown.

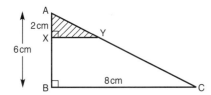

Find the distance of the centre of gravity of the remaining lamina from: (a) BC; (b) AB.

If the lamina is now suspended from C, find the angle that BC makes with the vertical.

5 A uniform, plane figure consists of a semicircular lamina of radius a and centre C, together with an isosceles triangle of base $2a$ and height $2a$. The two are connected by their common base line in the same plane on opposite sides of C.

Find the position of the centre of gravity from C.

6 A composite body consists of a uniform, solid hemisphere of radius a and a uniform, solid cylinder of base radius a and height h. The two are made of the same material and are connected by their common base.

If the body is in equilibrium when any part of the hemispherical surface is in contact with a horizontal table, find the height of the cylinder in terms of a.

7 The diagram shows a uniform square lamina ABCD of side $6a$.

The mid-point of AD is E and the point G is the centre of gravity of triangle CDE.

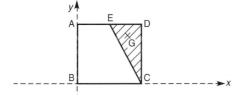

Find the coordinates of G with respect to the axes shown.

If the triangle CDE is now removed, find the centre of gravity of the remaining trapezium.

8 A uniform piece of wire is bent into the form of the letter 'P'.

If the radius of the semicircular part is a and the length of the stem of the letter is $4a$, find the centre of gravity of the figure.

If the 'letter' is now suspended from its free end, find the angle that the stem makes with the vertical, answering to the nearest degree.

9 A hollow, hemispherical shell of radius a has a flat, circular base made of the same material as the shell. The thickness is uniform throughout. The object is now suspended from a point on the circumference of the base.

Find, to the nearest degree, the angle that the base makes with the vertical.

10 A composite body consists of a uniform, solid, circular cylinder of height $4a$ and base radius a, together with a uniform, solid, right circular cone of height $2a$ and base radius a. They are made of the same material and are joined by their common base.

Find the distance of the centre of gravity from the common base.

11 A letter 'T' is made out of uniform, thin wire as shown in the diagram.

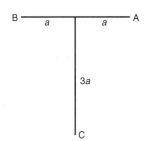

Find the distance of the centre of gravity of the framework from AB.

If the framework is now freely suspended from A, find the angle that AB makes with the vertical, answering to the nearest degree.

A small particle of weight w is now attached to the framework at C and it is found that, when the framework is again freely suspended from A, the side AB now makes an angle of $45°$ with the vertical.

Taking the weight of the original framework to be W, find w in terms of W.

12 A composite body is made up of a solid cylinder of base radius a and height $6a$, together with a solid cone of base radius a and height $4a$, the two being fixed together by their common base. They are both uniform and made of the same material.

Find the distance of the centre of gravity from the common base.

The body is now placed on an inclined plane with the free base of the cylinder in contact with the plane.

Find, to the nearest degree, the inclination of the plane to the horizontal if the body is on the point of tilting over. You may assume the plane is rough enough to prevent the body sliding.

Chapter 16

Statics

This chapter deals with bodies in equilibrium under the action of coplanar forces.

It introduces the concept of taking moments.

Moment of a force F about a point A $= F \times$ perpendicular distance from A.

> Resolve in a suitable direction.
> Resolve in a perpendicular direction.
> Take moments about a suitable point.

Examples

EXAMPLE

1

A small, uniform ladder AB of mass 20 kg rests with its end B on rough, horizontal ground, 0.6 m from the base of a vertical wall. The other end A of the ladder rests against the wall at a point 1.4 m from its base. The ladder rests in a vertical plane perpendicular to the wall.

Assuming the wall is smooth, find: (a) the magnitude of the friction force at the base of the ladder; (b) the least value of the coefficient of friction between the ground and the ladder.

SOLUTION

Resolve vertically

$R = 20g$.

Resolve horizontally

$F = S$.

Moments about B

$S \times 1.4 = 20g \times 0.3$

$\underline{S = 42}$.

For equilibrium we require $F \leq \mu R$

$$\mu \geq \frac{42}{20g}$$

$$\mu \geq \frac{3}{14}.$$

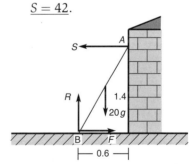

(a) The magnitude of the friction force $= \underline{\underline{42\,\text{N}}}$.

(b) The least value of $\underline{\underline{\mu = \frac{3}{14}}}$.

EXAMPLE

2

A uniform plank AB of mass 100 kg and length 4 m rests horizontally on two supports C and D, C being 0.5 m from A, and D being 1.5 m from B.

Find: (a) the reaction of the support at C; (b) the reaction of the support at D.

SOLUTION

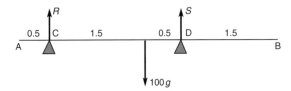

Moments about C

$S \times 2 = 100g \times 1.5$

$S = 735.$

Resolve vertically

$S + R = 100g$

$R = 245.$

(a) The reaction at C = 245 N.
(b) The reaction at D = 735 N.

EXAMPLE

3

A uniform plank AB of length 12 m and mass 40 kg rests horizontally on two supports C and D at equal distances *d* metres from each end of the plank. A man of mass 160 kg walks from the centre of the plank to one end.

Find the maximum value of *d* if the plank is not to tilt.

SOLUTION

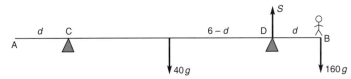

If the plank is on the point of tilting when the man is at the end, the reaction of one support will be zero.

Moments about D

$40g \times (6 - d) = 160g \times d$

$240 - 40d = 160d$

$d = 1.2.$

The maximum value of $d = 1.2\,\text{m}$.

EXAMPLE

4

A rigid steel bar AB of length 10 m and mass 30 kg is supported in a horizontal position by two vertical ropes XA and YB, attached to the ends of the bar. A gymnast of mass 50 kg is hanging on to the bar at a point C of the bar, such that the tension in the rope XA is three times the tension in YB.

By modelling the steel bar as a uniform rod and the gymnast as a particle, find the distance AC.

SOLUTION

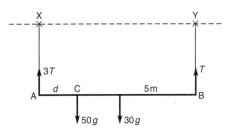

Let the tensions in the strings be T and $3T$ and the distance $AC = d$.

Moments about A

$T \times 10 = (30g \times 5) + (50g \times d)$

$\quad 200 = 150 + 50d$

$\quad\quad 50 = 50d$

$\quad\quad\underline{d = 1}.$

Resolve vertically

$4T = 80g$

$\underline{T = 20g}.$

The distance of the gymnast from the end A of the bar $= \underline{1\,\text{m}}$.

EXAMPLE

5

A uniform rod AB of length $4a$ and weight W is smoothly hinged at a point A on a vertical wall. A light rope is attached to the other end B of the bar and by this to a point C on the wall at a vertical distance of $3a$ from A so that the rod is horizontal.

Find the tension in the rope in terms of W.

If a mass of weight w is now attached to the rod at B and it is known that the breaking strength of the rope is $2W$, find the maximum value of w in terms of W.

SOLUTION

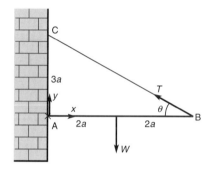

We can resolve T into two components, $T \cos \theta$ horizontally and $T \sin \theta$ vertically.

Moments about A   (without the mass attached)

$T \sin \theta \times 4a = W \times 2a$

$\quad \tfrac{12}{5} T = 2W$

$\quad\quad \underline{T = \tfrac{5}{6} W}.$

Moments about A   (with mass attached)

$W \times 2a + w \times 4a = 2W \sin \theta \times 4a$

$\quad\quad 2w = \tfrac{7}{5} W$

$\quad\quad \underline{w = 0.7W}.$

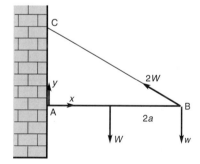

(a) The tension in the string without the mass attached $= \underline{5W/6}$.

(b) The maximum value of $\underline{w = 0.7W}$.

EXAMPLE

6

A uniform rod AB of length $6a$ and weight W has its end A on rough, horizontal ground and a point C of its length, where $AC = 5a$, resting on top of a smooth, vertical fence of height $3a$. The rod rests in a vertical plane perpendicular to the fence. Find in terms of W: (a) the reaction of the top of the fence on the rod; (b) the normal contact force of the ground on the rod.

If in this position the rod is on the point of slipping, find: (c) the value of the coefficient of friction μ between the ground and the rod.

SOLUTION

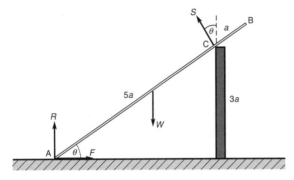

Moments about A

$S \times 5a = W \times 3a \times \cos\theta$

$5S = W \times 3 \times \frac{4}{5}$

$S = \frac{12}{25}W.$

Resolve vertically

$S\cos\theta + R = W$

$R = W - \frac{12}{25}W \times \frac{4}{5}$

$R = \frac{77}{125}W.$

Resolve horizontally

$F = S\sin\theta$

$F = \frac{12}{25}W \times \frac{3}{5}$

$F = \frac{36}{125}W.$

If the rod is on the point of slipping,

$F = \mu R$

$\frac{36}{125}W = \mu \times \frac{77}{125}W$

$\mu = \frac{36}{77}.$

(a) The reaction of the top of the fence $= \frac{12}{25}W.$

(b) The normal contact force at the ground is $\dfrac{77W}{125}.$

(c) The value of $\mu = \frac{36}{77}.$

EXAMPLE

7

A uniform, solid hemisphere of radius a and weight W rests on rough, horizontal ground and against a smooth, vertical wall, as shown in the diagram. The plane face of the hemisphere makes an angle of 30° with the horizontal.

If the hemisphere is on the point of slipping, find the value of μ, the coefficient of friction between it and the ground.

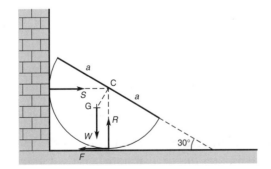

SOLUTION The centre of gravity of a solid hemisphere lies $\frac{3}{8}a$ from the centre of its base, i.e. CG $= \frac{3}{8}a$.

Moments about C	*Resolve vertically*	*Resolve horizontally*
$F \times a = W \times \frac{3}{8}a \sin 30°$	$R = W.$	$F = S.$
$\underline{F = \frac{3}{16}W.}$		

If the hemisphere is on the point of slipping,

$$F = \mu R$$

$$\tfrac{3}{16}W = \mu W$$

$$\underline{\mu = \tfrac{3}{16}.}$$

The value of the coefficient of friction $\underline{\underline{\mu = \tfrac{3}{16}}}$.

Exercises

1 A uniform ladder AB of mass 50 kg rests with its base B 90 cm from the bottom of a smooth, vertical wall. The other end A of the ladder rests against the wall at a height of 6 m from the ground. The ladder rests in a vertical plane perpendicular to the wall.

Find: (a) the reaction of the wall on the ladder; (b) the normal contact force of the ground on the ladder; (c) the least value of μ, the coefficient of friction.

2 A uniform rod AB has a length of 10 m and mass 18 kg. A particle P of mass 2 kg is attached to the rod at A.

If the rod now rests horizontally on a single support C, find the distance of C from the end A.

3 A uniform plank AB of length 10 m and mass 60 kg rests on two supports C and D, which are 6 m apart. When a boy weighing 40 kg sits on the end B of the plank, it is on the point of tilting.

By modelling the plank as a uniform rod and the boy as a particle, find the distances of the supports from the end B.

4 A uniform plank AB of weight W and length $6a$ rests horizontally on two supports, one at the end A and the other at a point C, where AC $= 4a$. A man weighing $2W$ stands on the plank at a point between A and C, so that his distance from A is d. The maximum load that the support at A can bear is $2W$.

By modelling the plank as a rod and the boy as a particle, show that $d \le \frac{1}{2}a$.

If in fact $d = \frac{1}{2}$ and the man begins to walk slowly along the plank towards B, show that he can only walk a distance $4a$ before the equilibrium of the plank is destroyed.

5 A rigid bar AB of length 8 m and mass 20 kg is supported at its ends by two light, vertical ropes XA and YB. A box of mass 100 kg is hung from the bar by a light chain attached to a point C of the bar, such that AC = 1.12 m.

Find the ratio of the tensions in the ropes YB and XA.

6 A uniform rigid rod of length $8a$ and weight $5\sqrt{3}W$ has its end A resting against a smooth, vertical wall and is inclined at 60° to the upward vertical. It is kept in this position by resting on a small smooth peg P, as shown in the diagram. The rod lies in a plane perpendicular to the wall.

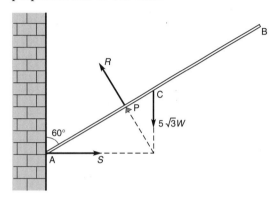

Find: (a) the distance AP; (b) the reactions at A and P.

7 A uniform, smooth, solid sphere of weight W and radius $5a$ rests on a smooth plane inclined at θ to the horizontal, where $\tan\theta = \frac{5}{12}$. The sphere is kept in equilibrium on the inclined plane by means of an inextensible string AB of length $8a$, attached to the sphere's surface at A, and the other end B of the string is fastened to a point on the plane up a line of greatest slope.

Show that when the sphere is in equilibrium: (a) the string is horizontal; (b) the tension in the string is $\frac{5}{12}W$.

8 A smooth, glass bowl is in the shape of a hollow hemisphere and rests on a horizontal table. The circular rim of the bowl has a radius of 12 cm and is parallel to the surface of the table. A smooth, uniform, glass rod PQ of mass m is placed so that it is partly inside and partly outside the bowl. Its end P rests on the inside surface of the bowl and a point R of the rod rests against the rim of the bowl.

If the rod makes an angle of 19° with the horizontal, find its length, assuming the bowl remains in its original position.

Answers

1 Constant acceleration

(1) (a) 160 m.   Use $s = ut + \frac{1}{2}at^2$.
    (b) 0.4 m s^{-2}.   Use $v = u + at$.

(2) (a) $u = 23$ m s^{-1}.   Use $s = ut + \frac{1}{2}at^2$ for motion from A to B.
                       Use $s = ut + \frac{1}{2}at^2$ for motion from A to C.
    (b) Retardation $= 1$ m s^{-2}.   Solve the two equations.
    (c) Speed at B $= 17$ m s^{-1}.   Use $v = u + at$.
         Speed at C $= 13$ m s^{-1}.

(3) (a) 4 m s^{-2}.   Use $v = u + at$.
    (b) XY $= 800$ m.   Use $s = \frac{1}{2}(u + v)t$.

The car *does* overtake the cyclist, who has travelled only 750 m in 25 s.

(4) (a) 5 m s^{-1}.   Use $s = ut + \frac{1}{2}at^2$ for motion from O to A.
                       Use $s = ut + \frac{1}{2}at^2$ for motion from O to B.
    (b) 10 m s^{-2}.   Solve the two equations.

(5) (a) 15 s.
    (b) 10 m s^{-2}.   Take each section of motion separately.

(6) (a) 15 s.   Use $s = ut + \frac{1}{2}at^2$ for both stones.
    (b) 2205 m.

(7) (a) 5 m s^{-2}.   Use $s = ut + \frac{1}{2}at^2$ for motion from A to B.
                       Use $s = ut + \frac{1}{2}at^2$ for motion from A to C.
    (b) 70 m s^{-1}.   Solve the two equations.

(8) (a) 90 s.   Equate the times, equate the distances.
    (b) $T = 10$ s.

2 Friction

(1) Max $a = 14°$.   Resolve parallel and perpendicular to the plane.
                     Use $F = \mu R$.

(2) (a) 4.0768 N.   Resolve parallel and perpendicular to the plane.
                     Friction acting *up* the plane.
    (b) 5.3312 N.   Resolve parallel and perpendicular to the plane.
                     Friction acting *down* the plane.

Answers

(3)   Smallest force $= 0.99$ N.   Resolve parallel and perpendicular to the plane.
Friction acting *up* the plane.

(4)   (a) $40°$.   Resolve horizontally and vertically.
Take moments.

       (b) 70.56 N.

(5)   Using the method of (4) show that $\tan a \leq 1 \implies$ hence result.

       Lightest boy $= 50$ kg.   Method as in first part but with extra mg at the base of the ladder.

(6) $7g/20$.   Resolve parallel and perpendicular to the plane.

(7) $45°$.   Resolve parallel and perpendicular to the plane and eliminate P.

(8) $\mu = \frac{2}{3}$.   Resolve vertically for Q.
Resolve vertically and horizontally for P. Friction limiting.

(9) $\mu = 0.117$.   Resolve perpendicular and parallel to the plane.

3   Newton's laws of motion

(1)   (a) $0.3 \, \text{m s}^{-2}$.   Set up the equation of motion.
       (b) $108 \, \text{km h}^{-1}$ $(30 \, \text{m s}^{-1})$.   Use $v = u + at$.
       (c) 1500 m.   Use $s = \frac{1}{2}(u+v)t$.

(2)   (a) 37.5 kg.   Equation of motion upwards to find the reaction on the boy: $R = 367.5$ N; now divide by 9.8.
       (b) 32.5 kg.   Equation of motion downwards to find the reaction on the boy: $R = 318.5$ N; now divide by 9.8.

(3) 3040 N.   Equation of motion up the plane.
       $0.25 \, \text{m s}^{-2}$.   New equation of motion up the plane.

(4)   (a) 3 s.   Use $s = ut + \frac{1}{2}at^2$.
       (b) 3.36 N.   From the equations of motion for the two particles.
       (c)   extra time $= 3/7$ s;   From the free motion of A, using $v = u + at$.
            1.5 m below P.

(5)   (a) $4.2 \, \text{m s}^{-2}$.   Set up the equations of motion.
       (b) 5.04 N.   From the equation of motion.
       (c) $4.2 \, \text{m s}^{-1}$.   Set up the new equation of motion for A now the string is slack and then use $v^2 = u^2 + 2as$ with $s = 9$ m.

Answers

(6) (a) $1.96\,\mathrm{m\,s^{-2}}$.　　Set up the equations of motion and include $F = \mu R$.

(b) $4.704\,\mathrm{N}$.　　From the equations of motion.

No.　　Particle A travels $8\,\mathrm{m}$ up the plane while the string is taut and then just over $2\,\mathrm{m}$ when the string is slack — a total distance of just over $10\,\mathrm{m}$ up the plane.

(7) (a) $5.6\,\mathrm{m\,s^{-1}}$.　　Use $v^2 = u^2 + 2as$ with $a = 0.8g$.

(b) $8\,\mathrm{m}$.　　Retardation $= \mu g$.

Assumptions:　child modelled as particle, no air resistance; child starts from rest at A.

4　Impulse, momentum and kinetic energy

(1) $22.5\,\mathrm{m\,s^{-1}}$　　Use impulse = change in momentum.

(2) (a) $2.5\,\mathrm{m}$.　　Find the speed when the particle reaches the ground $= 14\,\mathrm{m\,s^{-1}}$, using $v^2 = u^2 + 2as$.

(b) $0.63\,\mathrm{N\,s}$.　　Use impulse = change in momentum.

(3) (a) $4\,\mathrm{m\,s^{-1}}$.　　Use conservation of momentum.

(b) $20m\,\mathrm{N\,s}$.　　Use impulse = change in momentum.

(4) (a) $3\,\mathrm{m\,s^{-1}}$.　　Use conservation of momentum.

(b) $20m\,\mathrm{N\,s}$.　　Find change in momentum for B.

(c) $140m\,\mathrm{J}$.　　Find *KE* before and *KE* after.

(5) (a) $2\,\mathrm{m\,s^{-1}}$.　　Use conservation of momentum.

(b) $0.6\,\mathrm{N\,s}$.　　Use impulse equation for B.

(c) Impulse in AB $= 0.5\,\mathrm{N\,s}$;　　Conservation of momentum gives the final speed to impulse in BC $= 0.2\,\mathrm{N\,s}$.　be $1\,\mathrm{m\,s^{-1}}$.

(6) (a) $2\,\mathrm{m\,s^{-1}}$.　　Use conservation of momentum.

(b) $1206\,\mathrm{J}$.　　$KE = 0$ before, find *KE* after.

(c) $375\,\mathrm{N}$.　　Find the retardation of the rifle using $v^2 = u^2 + 2as$.

(7) $x = 0.3\,\mathrm{kg}$.　　Use conservation of momentum.

$u = 30\,\mathrm{m\,s^{-1}}$.　　Equate the loss in *KE* to 378.

(8) First impulse $6.3\,\mathrm{N\,s}$.　　Impulse = change in momentum.

Second impulse $= 5.04\,\mathrm{N\,s}$.

(9) (a) $0.4\,\mathrm{m\,s^{-1}}$.　　Conservation of momentum.

(b) $0.24\,\mathrm{N\,s}$.　　Impulse = change in momentum for Q.

(c) $0.336\,\mathrm{J}$.

(d) $0.522\,\mathrm{s}$.

Answers

5 ## Work and power

(1) 4.05 kN.

Use work done = change in *KE* or find its acceleration using $v^2 = u^2 + 2as$.

(2) 19.9 kW.

Find the tractive force from the equation of motion. Use power = tractive force × velocity.

(3) (a) 7.6 kW.
(b) 12.16 m s^{-1}.

At steady speed tractive force = resistance. Use power = tractive force × velocity.

(4) (a) 60 N.

Work done = $(T - R) \times 1000$. Equate this to the gain in *KE*.

(b) 450 W.

Use power = tractive force × velocity.

(5) (a) 9 kN.

Equation of motion up the plane to find the tractive force.

(b) 112.5 kW.
(c) 72 km h^{-1} (20 m s^{-1}).

Power = tractive force × velocity. At maximum speed, forces up the plane balance forces down the plane.

(6) (a) 750 kW.
(b) 0.05 m s^{-2}.
(c) Power = 900 kW.

Power = tractive force × velocity. Set up the equation of motion. Show that $v = 30$.

(7) (a) 96 km h^{-1}.
(b) 57.6 km h^{-1}.

(8) 450 kJ.

Show that the speed uphill is 20 m s^{-1}.

6 ## Projectiles

(1) (a) 3 s.
(b) 58.8 m.
(c) 11.025 m.

Consider vertical motion and then horizontal motion.

(2) (a) 30°.
(b) $10\sqrt{3}$ m = 17.3 m (three significant figures).

Consider vertical motion to find the angle. Consider horizontal motion to find the range.

(3) (a) 5 s.
(b) $1\frac{3}{7}$ s.
(c) 90 m.

Consider vertical motion.

Answers

(4) (a) 3 s.

Consider vertical motion with a height of 14.7 m (16 m − 1.3 m).

(b) 102 m (three significant figures).

Consider horizontal motion.

(5) $250 \, \text{m s}^{-1}$.

From horizontal motion $Vt = 1000$.
Use $s = ut + \frac{1}{2}at^2$ for vertical motion.
Eliminate Vt from the two equations.

(6) —

Find expressions for the times for each and hence find the ranges.
Consider vertical motion to find the maximum heights.

(7) (a) 14 s.
(b) $99 \, \text{m s}^{-1}$.

Let both horizontal and vertical components be V and then consider vertical and horizontal motions.

(8) $V = 28 \, \text{m s}^{-1}$.

Find expressions for the greatest height and the range.
Use the result $H = V^2 \sin^2 \theta / 2g$.

(9) (a) 20 s.
(b) 3.395 km from O.

Consider vertical motion with $s = ut + \frac{1}{2}at^2$.
Find the horizontal distance of the aircraft from O when the case drops, and the further horizontal distance travelled by the suitcase.

7 Impact

(1) (a) $1 \, \text{m s}^{-1}$.

Momentum is conserved.

(b) $e = 1/8$.

Use Newton's experimental law.

(2) (a) A's speed $= u$;
B's speed $= 7u/2$.

Momentum is conserved and Newton's experimental law.

(b) $9mu$.

Impulse = change in momentum.
Show that A's speed is greater than that of the combined particle.

(3) (a) A's speed $= 32 \, \text{m s}^{-1}$;
B's speed $= 42 \, \text{m s}^{-1}$.

Conservation of momentum.
Newton's experimental law.

(b) A's speed $= 32 \, \text{m s}^{-1}$;
B's speed $= 21 \, \text{m s}^{-1}$;
C's speed $= 28 \, \text{m s}^{-1}$.

(4) —

Use conservation of momentum and Newton's experimental law.

Answers

(5) —

Use conservation of momentum and Newton's experimental law.

(6) A's speed $= u/3$ in opposite direction.
B's speed $= 2u/3$.
B's speed after hitting barrier $= u/2$.

(7) A's speed $= 0$.
$(2 - 4e)/3$.

Conservation of momentum.
B's speed after 2nd collision $= 2(1 - 2e)/3$.
If $e > \frac{1}{2}$ then B's speed is negative and thus there is a further collision.

---

8 Motion in a horizontal circle

(1) (a) $\frac{1}{2}\pi = 1.57\,\mathrm{rad\,s}^{-1}$.
(b) $0.308\,\mathrm{N}$.

15 circles per min $= 15/60 \times 2\pi\,\mathrm{rad\,s}^{-1}$.
Use radial equation of motion.

(2) (a) $16\pi/3 = 16.76\,\mathrm{rad\,s}^{-1}$.
(b) $20\,\mathrm{cm}$.

Use $R = mrw^2$, where $m = 0.36$.

(3) (a) Radius $= 5a$.
(b) $13mg/12$.
(c) $2\pi\sqrt{(10a/3g)}$.

Use Pythagoras.
Resolve vertically and use radial equation of motion.

(4) (a) Tension in AC $= 2.5mg$;
tension in BC $= 0.5mg$.
(b) $\min w = \sqrt{(2g/a)}$.

Resolve vertically and
use radial equation of motion.

(5) (a) Radius $= 3a$.
(b) $3mg/4$.
(c) $2mg/5$.

Use Pythagoras.
Resolve vertically and use radial equation of motion.

(6) (a) $2mg, 4mg$.
(b) $\sqrt{2}mg$.
(c) $\sqrt{(3\sqrt{2}g/a)}$.

Resolve vertically and use radial equation of motion.

(7) $22.5°$.

$454\,\mathrm{N}$.

Resolve vertically and use radial equation of motion and then divide.
Set up new radial equation of motion and resolve vertically.

(8) $v = \sqrt{(gd)}$.

Resolve vertically and radial equation of motion.

Answers

9

Motion in a vertical circle

(1) $V = \sqrt{(7ag/2)}$.

Use conservation of energy and radial equation of motion.

(2) $\theta = \cos^{-1}(2/3) \approx 48°$.

Use conservation of energy and radial equation of motion.

(3) $V/2$.
$4\sqrt{(ag)}$.

Use conservation of momentum.
Use conservation of energy and radial equation of motion.

(4) (a) $\frac{1}{2}mg$.
(b) $\sqrt{(ag)}$.
(c) $2mg$.

Resolve vertically and radial equation of motion.
Use conservation of energy.
Use radial equation of motion.

(5) (a) $\sqrt{(7ag\sin\theta)}$.
(b) $3mg\sin\theta$.

Use conservation of energy.
Radial equation of motion.

(6) —

Use conservation of energy and radial equation of motion to show $\theta = 120°$ when $R = 0$.
For greatest height use $v^2 = u^2 + 2as$ considering vertical motion from the point where $R = 0$.

(7) (a) —

Use conservation of energy and radial equation of motion.

(b) —

Use energy considerations from start to finish.

(8) (a) $u = 7\,\mathrm{m\,s^{-1}}$.

Energy considerations from A to B.
Work done against friction equals change in KE from B to C.

(b) 70.7 %.

Just before B: $R - mg = mv^2/12$.
Just after B: $R = mg$.

(9) $2.8\,\mathrm{m\,s^{-1}}$.

Use conservation of energy.
Use conservation of momentum on impact.
Use conservation of energy again.

10

Newton's law of gravitation

(1) (a) 113 km.
(b) 7.84 km s^{-1}.

Evaluate r using $r^3 = GM/w^2$.
Use $v = rw$, where $r = 6513$ and $w = \pi/2610$.

(2) 573 km.

Evaluate r using $r^3 = GM/w^2$ and then subtract Mercury's radius.

Answers

(3) $3.57 \, \text{km s}^{-1}$.

Use $w^2 = GM/r^3$ and then $v = rw$, where $r = 3500$ and $w = 0.001021$.

(4) (a) $v = \sqrt{\left(\dfrac{2gR^2}{x} + u^2 - 2gR\right)}$. Write the acceleration in the form $v \dfrac{dv}{dx}$.

(b) $2.36 \, \text{km s}^{-1}$.

As $x \to \infty$, u^2 must always remain positive, i.e. $u^2 > 2gR$.

(5) We need to calculate M (the mass of the planet).

Ratio of the radii (planet : Earth) $= 80 : 6400$.

$$= 1 : 80.$$

Hence the ratio of their masses $= 1 : 80^3$.

It follows the mass of the planet $= \dfrac{6 \times 10^{24}}{80^3}$

$$= 1.172 \times 10^{19} \, \text{kg}.$$

(6) Approx. $690 \, \text{m s}^{-1}$.

As $x \to \infty$, $v^2 \to U^2 - 2GM/R$.

11 Elasticity

(1) Modulus $= 2g = 19.6 \, \text{N}$.

Equate forces in equilibrium and use Hooke's law.

(2) (a) $4mg/5$ (inelastic); $3mg/5$ (elastic).

Resolve horizontally and resolve vertically.

(b) $3mg$.

Use Hooke's law.

(3) (a) $a/40$.

Equate forces in equilibrium and use Hooke's law.

(b) $5a/4$.

Use conservation of energy from top to bottom.

(4) $7.5 \, \text{kN}$.

Find the *KE* lost by the train and equate it to final energy stored in the buffers. Finally use Hooke's law.

(5) $10 \, \text{cm}$.

Equate the work done by the limiting friction force to the change in elastic energy of the mass.

(6) $p = 15/8 = 1.875$.

The particle drops $1.2 \, \text{m}$ — hence the diagram has two $5-12-13$ right-angled triangles. Equate the energy stored in the strings to the loss in *PE*.

(7) Extension $= a/12$.

Resolve vertically and Hooke's law.

(a) $5/2\sqrt{(ag/3)}$.

Use energy considerations throughout.

(b) $\sqrt{(2ag)}$.

(8) $2 : 3$.

Use work done = change in energy for each spider separately.

Answers

12 Simple harmonic motion

(1) (a) Max. speed $= 2\sqrt{(ag/3)}$. From SHM equation $w^2 = g/3a$.
(b) Max. force $= 2mg/3$. Max. acceleration $= aw^2$.
(c) $T = 2\pi\sqrt{(3a/g)}$. $T = 2\pi/w$.

(2) (a) 30 cm. Amplitude $= \frac{1}{2}$ (dist. between points).
(b) $T = 6$ s. $T = 2\pi/w$.
(c) Max. $KE = m\pi^2/200$ J. Max. $KE = \frac{1}{2}m(aw)^2$.

(3) (a) $4\pi/15$ m s^{-1}. Max. speed $= aw$.
(b) Max. force $= 8\pi^2/45$ N. Max. acceleration $= aw^2$.
(c) Max. $KE = 8\pi^2/45$ J. Max. $KE = \frac{1}{2}m(aw)^2$.
(d) $\sqrt{3}$ m. Use $v^2 = w^2(a^2 - x^2)$.
(e) $2\frac{1}{2}$ s. Use $t = 1/w \sin^{-1}(x/a)$.

(4) (a) 13 cm. Use $v^2 = w^2(a^2 - x^2)$ twice and solve the resulting equations.
(b) Max. speed $= 13$ m s^{-1}. Max. speed $= aw$.
(c) $T = \pi/50$ s. $T = 2\pi/w$.

(5) $2\pi/3 \sqrt{(a/2g)}$. From the SHM equation $w^2 = 2g/a$.

(6) (a) Max. $KE = \frac{1}{2}\pi^2$ J. Max. $KE = \frac{1}{2}m(aw)^2$.
(b) $\sqrt{3}\pi/6$ m s^{-1}. Use $v^2 = w^2(a^2 - x^2)$.
(c) 2 s. Use $t = 1/w \sin^{-1}(x/a)$.
(d) $2\sqrt{3}$ m. Use $v^2 = w^2(a^2 - x^2)$.

(7) (a) 2 m s^{-1}. Use conservation of energy.
(b) 1.4 m.

(8) (a) $3a/2$ below A. Equate forces parallel to the plane and use Hooke's law.
(b) a. Use conservation of energy.
(c) $\frac{1}{4}mga$. Max. $KE = \frac{1}{2}m(aw)^2$.

(9) (a) Amplitude $= 2$ m. $a = -32 \sin 4t$.
$x = \quad 2 \sin 4t$.
(b) 8 m s^{-1}. Max. speed occurs when $t = 0$.
(c) 16 N. Max. acceleration $= aw^2$.

13 Variable accelerations

(1) (a) $t = 4$ and $t = 7$ s. $v = 6t^2 - 66t + 168$.
(b) $t = 4$, $x = 272$ m
$t = 7$, $x = 245$ m.

Answers

(c) $t = 4$, $a = -18\,\mathrm{m\,s}^{-2}$; $\quad$ $a = 12t - 66$.
$\quad$ $t = 7$, $a = +18\,\mathrm{m\,s}^{-2}$.

(2) $\quad$ (a) $t = 3$ and $t = 7$ s. $\qquad$ $v = 3t^2 - 30t + 63$.
$\qquad$ (b) 32 m. $\qquad\qquad\qquad$ $t = 3$, $s = 81$.
$\qquad\qquad\qquad\qquad\qquad\qquad$ $t = 7$, $s = 49$.

(3) $\quad$ 250 m. $\qquad\qquad\qquad\qquad$ $v = 6t - 0.3t^2/2$.
$\qquad\qquad\qquad\qquad\qquad\qquad$ $s = 3t^2 - 0.3t^3/6$.

(4) $\quad$ (a) $3.06\,\mathrm{m\,s}^{-1}$.
$\qquad$ (b) 0.280 m. $\qquad\qquad\qquad$ $10s = \frac{1}{2}e^{2t} - 6t^2 - \frac{1}{2}$.
$\qquad$ (c) 0.896 s. $\qquad\qquad\qquad$ $10a = 2e^{2t} - 12$.

(5) $\quad$ (a) $x = 12$, $v = 34\,\mathrm{m\,s}^{-1}$. $\quad$ $v^2 = 2(x^3 - x^2 + 12x + 2)$.
$\qquad$ (b) $x = 57$, $v = 344\,\mathrm{m\,s}^{-1}$.

(6) $\quad$ $p = 4975$, $q = 20.5$. $\qquad$ Tractive force = power/speed.
$\qquad$ 21 min 48 s. $\qquad\qquad\qquad$ Set up equation of motion using $\mathrm{d}v/\mathrm{d}t$ for the
$\qquad\qquad\qquad\qquad\qquad\qquad$ acceleration.
$\qquad\qquad\qquad\qquad\qquad\qquad$ Separate the variables and integrate.

(7) $\quad$ — $\qquad\qquad\qquad\qquad\qquad$ Set up the equation of motion using $\mathrm{d}v/\mathrm{d}t$ for the
$\qquad\qquad\qquad\qquad\qquad\qquad$ acceleration.

(8) $\quad$ 14.4 s. $\qquad\qquad\qquad\qquad$ Separate the variables and integrate.

(9) $\quad$ Terminal speed $= \sqrt{(g/k)}$.
$\qquad$ 28.8 m. $\qquad\qquad\qquad\qquad$ Set up the equation of motion, separate the variables
$\qquad\qquad\qquad\qquad\qquad\qquad$ and integrate.
$\qquad\qquad\qquad\qquad\qquad\qquad$ $s = 1/(2k)\ln(4/3)$.

14 $\quad$ Vector mechanics

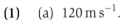

(1) $\quad$ (a) $120\,\mathrm{m\,s}^{-1}$. $\qquad\qquad$ $\boldsymbol{v} = 6t^2\boldsymbol{i} - 18t\boldsymbol{j}$.
$\qquad$ (b) $t = 2$, $a = 30\,\mathrm{m\,s}^{-2}$. $\qquad$ $\boldsymbol{a} = 12t\boldsymbol{i} - 18\boldsymbol{j}$.

(2) $\quad$ (a) $t = 8$, $v = 208\,\mathrm{m\,s}^{-1}$. $\quad$ $\boldsymbol{v} = 3t^2\boldsymbol{i} + (14t - 192)\boldsymbol{j}$.
$\qquad$ (b) $t = 8$, $a = 50\,\mathrm{m\,s}^{-2}$. $\qquad$ $\boldsymbol{a} = 6t\boldsymbol{i} + 14\boldsymbol{j}$.

(3) $\quad$ (a) $t = 8$ s. $\qquad\qquad\qquad$ $\boldsymbol{v} = (6t^2 - 30t)\boldsymbol{i} + (6t - 48)\boldsymbol{j}$.
$\qquad\qquad\qquad\qquad\qquad\qquad$ (a) The j component is zero.
$\qquad$ (b) $t = 0$ and $t = 5$ s. $\qquad$ (b) The i component is zero.
$\qquad$ (c) $t = 2$ and $t = 4$ s. $\qquad$ (c) The i and j components are equal.

Answers

(4) 45°.

1 N s.

$K = 0.8i - 0.6j$.

(5) (a) $5i + 4j$.

(b) 6.34°

(three significant figures)

Impulse = change in momentum.

Original angle was 45°.

New angle $= \tan^{-1}\left(\frac{4}{5}\right) = 38.66°$.

(6) 17 N.

$P = 2i$; $Q = 6i + 15j$.

(7) (a) $t = 2$, $r = 9$ m.

(b) $t = 2$, $v = 9$ m s^{-1}.

$v = 2ti + j + 8k$.

(8) $r = 3i + 2j + 7k$.

Set up the two equations of the paths of P and Q and show that the two equations are consistent with the solution $t = 1$.

(9) $t = 2$, $v = 7$ m s^{-1}.

$P = i - 8j + 4k$.

$Q = 4ti$.

$a = (1 + 4t)i - 8j + 4k$.

$v = (t + 2t^2 - 8)i + (-8t + 10)j + (4t - 5)k$.

(10) (a) 13 m s^{-1}.

(b) 12 N s.

Impulse = change in momentum.

Centres of gravity

(1) $2a/3$.

$\theta = 37°$.

Take moments about the middle side.

$\tan\theta = a/(4a/3) = 0.75$.

(2) (a) 10.5 cm.

(b) 2 cm.

Moments about the shortest side.

Moments about the middle side.

(3) (a) 43/26 cm.

(b) 49/26 cm.

39°.

Moments about BC.

Moments about DC.

$\tan\theta = (49/26)/(61/26)$.

(4) (a) 5/3 cm.

(b) 26/9 cm.

18°.

Moments about BC.

Moments about AB.

$\tan\theta = (5/3)/(46/9)$.

(5) $0.1867a$ from the base.

Take moments about the common base.

(6) $h = a/\sqrt{2}$.

Centre of gravity must lie on the common base if equilibrium is maintained as needed.

Take moments about the common base.

Answers

(7) G$(5a, 4a)$.

G'$(7a/3, 8a/3)$.

Centre of gravity of a is at the intersection of its medians.

(8) G = $[2a/(\pi + 4)$, $(3\pi + 8)a/(\pi + 4)]$.

$7°$.

Take moments to find G.

(9) $18°$

$\tan\theta = (a/3)/a = 1/3$.

(10) $23a/14$.

Take moments about the common base.

(11) $9a/10$.

$42°$.

$w = W/20$.

Take moments about AB.
Take moments about vertical through A.
Take moments about vertical through A.

(12) $25a/11, 15°$.

G must lie vertically above the end of the base of the cylinder.

16 Statics

(1) (a) 36.75 N.

Resolve horizontally.
Resolve vertically.

(b) 490 N.
(c) $\mu = 0.075$.

Moments about base of ladder.
$\mu \geq F/R$ for equilibrium.

(2) 4.5 m from A.

Take moments about the support.

(3) 3 m and 9 m from B.

Moments about the support nearer to B.

(4) —

Moments about C.

(5) Ratio 1 : 4.

Take moments about A or B.
Resolve vertically.

(6) (a) AP = $3a$.
(b) Reaction of wall = $5W$; reaction of peg = $10W$.

Use similar triangles.
Resolve horizontally.
Resolve vertically.
Moments about the point A.

(7) (a) —
(b) $5W/12$.

Use Pythagoras $5-12-13$ triangle.
Take moments about the point of contact of the sphere with the plane.

(8) 40 cm.

Use the fact that there are only three forces acting on the rod and thus they are concurrent.
Now use trigonometry.